S.R. 92

D1588299

TREES, CHESTS & BOXES

TREES
CHESTS
&
BOXES

OF THE SIXTEENTH AND SEVENTEENTH CENTURIES

A.J. Conybeare
N.D.F., M.I.C.For.

Published in 1991 by
The Self Publishing Association Ltd
Units 7/10, Hanley Workshops
Hanley Swan, Worcs
A MEMBER OF

in conjunction with
A.J. Conybeare

© A.J. Conybeare 1991

*All rights reserved. No part of this book may be reproduced or transmitted
in any form or by any means, electronic or mechanical including photocopying,
recording or by any information storage and retrieval system without permission
in writing from the publisher.*

British Library Cataloguing-in-Publication Data:

A catalogue record for this book is available from
The British Library.

ISBN 1 85421 142 0

Designed and produced by Images Design & Print, Hanley Swan, Worcs.
Printed and Bound in Great Britain by Hartnolls Ltd, Bodmin, Cornwall.

Contents

To Shirley

Pedunculate Oak, from John Evelyn's "Silva", 1776.

Although every effort has been made to trace the copyright holders of some photographs, the author has been unable to do so. We would be grateful if the copyright holder would contact the publisher.

INTRODUCTION

So far as I can tell, nobody has yet looked at antique oak furniture with a view to determining the origin of the timber from which it was made, and yet much information as to the sources lies within the timber itself.

Variations in annual ring-width are easily seen in oak, but the method of construction of joined 16th and 17th Century furniture usually obscures the end-grain of the larger panels. The end-grain in the boards used to construct six-plank chests and table boxes however can be easily examined; hence this book.

The information locked up in the cross-section of a tree gives us not only the age of the tree, but with trees of some age the system employed in their past management can be determined; equally, a lack of management shows up in the annual rings. Each ring is virtually a photograph of the conditions which prevailed during the year in which it was laid down, and a sequence of rings can provide a great deal of information.

Variations in ring-widths not only tell us which years were periods of drought; they also give us an indication of periods when the tree slowed in growth due to competition from other trees, or grew more rapidly following thinning operations, or the cutting of competing coppice growth.

Our modern "high forest" system of oak management is only some three hundred years old and was not employed when the timber which is found in 16th and 17th Century furniture was laid down. Home-grown timber must have been processed very near to the woodland or coppice in which it grew and I believe that information from the annual ring sequences can provide clues to the locality in which various items were manufactured.

Interpreting this information is of course a different matter, and what follows is an attempt to gain useful data from timber which was felled and seasoned more than three centuries ago, and then made into chests and boxes.

I have included some information on tools, and the box-makers, and the

9

forms of decoration employed; I also suggest dates for each of the chests, desks, and table boxes illustrated towards the end of the book, in the hope that this "background" information may make it easier to appreciate the items themselves. I make no apology for the amount of pure speculation; by the law of averages some of this must be valid. I will leave the reader to decide which.

A.J. Conybeare.

May 1990

Mature wood-pasture oak in the Forest of Dean, Gloucestershire.

THE TIMBER

Despite the vast store of myth and legend surrounding the oak in Britain, there is no proof that it is a truly native tree, although it was in the British Isles at least 5,000 years ago.

There are two species: the common or pedunculate oak, and the sessile or Durmast oak. Both occur in all parts of the country, but pedunculate oak is the more common tree. Today, pedunculate oak tends to be the overstorey in mixed woodland or the remaining coppice areas; sessile oak occurs more often in pure high forest and will tolerate lighter soils of more moderate fertility. Sessile oak is less prone to produce epicormic buds and produces longer lengths of knot-free timber.

Both species have virtually the same European distribution.

In Britain, occupying the more fertile lowland soils, oak was a natural competitor to an expanding human population, and as soon as man developed a primitive technology to clear it, it began to decline. As the human population rose, that of the oaks fell.

Given the primitive tools of early man and the difficulty in felling and removing such tough adversaries, it is not surprising that the trees soon became venerated and given magical properties. The Greeks believed that the oak was the first tree to be created and that the Gods had chosen it to be the medium whereby their wishes could be made known to the human race. Thus, the sacred oak grove at Dodona in Epirus was visited by people from all over Greece whenever they wished to know the will of Jupiter; their name for the tree was "Drys", from which came the Driads, attendants of the Goddess Artemis who were believed to live in woods. The Celtic Druids derived their name from "Derw" which was their name for the tree; the Saxons called it the "Aack", hence "acorn", the fruit of the Aack; in providing food for their pigs and timber for their fires and houses it lay at the very centre of their economy.

Once established, myths became deeply embedded in folk-lore. The

British yule log had its place in the pagan festival of Yule, which took place in December. Part of the Druids' mythology held that they alone could maintain perpetual fire; once a year all the fires of the people were put out, and rekindled from the sacred fires of the priests. The wood that they used was oak, which they believed carried eternally the spirit of Yule. The "Yule" log which was brought into the house to relight the winter fire was a part-burned log from the year before, carefully preserved. Right up to the Middle Ages and beyond, country people believed that some great misfortune would befall their household should any accident occur to the log between the annual fires.

When Edward II was born at Caernarvon Castle, it was deemed prudent to make his cradle of oak, the sacred timber of the Welsh, who still retained the beliefs of their ancestors, the Ancient Britons.

According to legend, King Arthur's great round table was made of oak.

With such an aura of mysticism, it is a wonder that any trees were cut at all, but in Britain the gradual erosion of the wild woodland continued as the human pressure increased. By the 6th century woodland still occupied perhaps a third of Britain; by 1086 A.D. this had fallen to fifteen percent. The natural regeneration of the wildwood was restricted by the grazing of cattle sheep and pigs in those areas to which they had access, but where access was denied, it became possible to manage woodland to obtain a reasonably sustained yield of timber by cutting areas regularly and allowing them to coppice. By the time of the Domesday survey about six villages in ten are recorded as having some woodland for local use. By this time, the practice of coppicing woodland appears to have been widespread, but this was still not the major use of wooded areas. Most of the remaining woodland appears to have been of the wood/pasture type with individual trees growing occasionally to a great size. As more and more land was cleared for agriculture and more wildwood converted to the coppice system of management, the old form of land use declined in area. By 1250, the Forest of Dean had been extensively coppiced and "pastured", but could still provide massive timbers from the remnants of the ancient woodland for the roof of the Dominican Friary at Gloucester.

By the 13th Century, a sort of balance seems to have occurred and the place of woodland in the English countryside had become established. There were considerable local variations; in places the landscape would have consisted, as it does today, of settled farmland with islands of scattered woodland on the less workable soils, in others the farmland would have appeared as glades in the ancient wooded areas.

Woodland used for the production of timber and underwood was by now very largely privately owned, very often by the Abbeys which prolifcrated throughout the countryside, and from about this time, woods began to be managed as a renewable natural resource; indeed whole rural communities depended upon them for material for house building, fencing, fuel, and fodder, not to mention the edible wildlife.

By medieval times, most managed woods were run on a coppice-with-standards system whereby a regular interval was established between cuttings which varied according to local needs. At each cutting of the poles and underwood, straight and vigorous stems were left at intervals to grow on into larger timber, whilst the cut over coppice regenerated beneath them. These stems, which on suitable soils were mainly of oak, produced periods of rapid growth when the competition from the cut coppice was less, slowing down as the regrowth thickened and made more demands on the available moisture and nutrients in the soil. At the next cutting of the understorey, growth in the remaining "standard" trees would again increase. Cross-sections of oak trees grown in these circumstances show these alternate periods of slow and fast growth in their annual rings. (Page 28) This system of Forestry produces oaks with relatively short boles of knot-free timber, with wide-spreading hemispherical crowns; diameter increase can be fast at perhaps five to six rings per inch on fertile sites. Such timber cleaves easily. (Page 30)

Later Forestry practice would have oaks planted densely in pure groups, each tree forcing the others higher and higher, and with proper management over a long period of time producing very long lengths of straight, knot-free timber. Groups of trees in a wildwood situation would produce similar timber unaided by the Forester, but their annual rings would not show the regular variation in rates of growth that coppice grown trees do, or that "modern" trees do after regular thinning.

The coppice cutting rotation appears to have varied from between five to ten years on the early coppice areas; such an operation would have ensured supplies of material of the correct size for local markets, the underwood providing small dimensioned produce such as hurdles, hetherings, wattle and firewood whereas the "standard" trees would have provided building materials of larger size. Ordinary medieval buildings contained large numbers of small oaks of between twenty and seventy years of age, rarely more than twenty feet long. Such timber would have been the typical produce of a coppice-with-standards system over many rotations of the understorey.

Between 1400 and 1700 pressures on the woodland areas began to increase dramatically. There was a rise in population which led to an increase in clearances for agriculture, and an increase in the demand for oak as people began to build larger houses, and to demand more possessions as their prosperity increased. Simultaneously the demand for timber as fuel increased, as did that for charcoal for industrial purposes.

Good woodland management under the sustained yield principle, together with an increase in planting could perhaps have coped with the increased demand, but the Dissolution of the Monasteries led to the breaking up of reasonable well managed woodland over quite large areas, and in the 16th and 17th Centuries conversion to agriculture accelerated. (By the late 18th Century, three quarters of the medieval woods in Norfolk had disappeared.)

Over this period there was a lengthening of the coppice rotation; what had been a seven year rotation in the 14th Century became a ten year rotation at the end of the 16th Century. It is possible that on some areas which had been continuously cut over for centuries a drop in productivity may have been caused by a decline in the fertility of the sites. Some 17th Century oak shows evidence of rotations of over thirty years.

Sheep grazing beneath oak in the Forest of Dean. The nearest tree is perhaps 150 years old and due to lack of competition is still growing at an even annual rate.

By the end of the 16th Century, what forest heritage remained began to dwindle rapidly; in 1548 the Government ordered an enquiry into the excessive consumption of timber by the iron foundries in Sussex, but to no effect. A number of Acts of Parliament attempted to prevent the cutting of timber for industrial purposes; in 1580 William Harrison reported that in places in England a man could ride for ten or twenty miles and find very little wood beyond that planted here and there beside new dwellings.

The first recorded post-medieval planting of oak trees was that by Lord Burleigh in Windsor Great Park in 1580, some of which are still alive. In 1611 Arthur Standish published the first English forestry pamphlet, but it was not until John Evelyn published his "Silva" in 1664 that planting of trees on a large scale was encouraged; by then it was too late. The planting of oak in the 17th Century became a country gentleman's hobby rather than a serious attempt to repair the damage of the past two centuries. In the early 17th Century Edmund Hawes wrote: "Such hath been the plenty of wood in England for all bless that, within man's memory, it was held impossible to have any want of wood in England. But contrary to former imaginations such hath been the great expense of wood to make household furniture, casks, and other vessels not to be numbered, and of carts, wagons and coaches, besides the extream waste of wood in making iron, burning of brick and tile, that at this present, through the great consuming of wood as aforesaid, and neglect of the planting of woods, there is so great a scarcity of wood throughout the whole kingdom . . ."

The industrial consumption of wood for charcoal used vast quantities in the manufacture of iron, in the 1630's supplies had dwindled to such a point that the smelting of iron to make cannon had to be curtailed; from being an exporter of cannon in the 16th Century, by 1630 the British were forced to import guns from Sweden, not having sufficient fuel to make their own. In 1631 Edmund Hawes was reporting such a scarcity of firewood that inhabitants throughout the whole kingdom were for the first time forced to burn sea-coal and mined coal in their houses. Between 1630 and 1670 the price of charcoal increased two and a half times.

Imported oak had been favoured for some uses since the 16th Century, but it is difficult to say whether oak was imported due entirely to shortages of the home-grown timber, or whether as a result of increased demand from an expanding and more prosperous population. John Evelyn said of the English oak "it is good for shingles, pales, laths, cooper's ware, clap-board for wainscott, and some panels curiously veined, of much esteem in former times till the finer grained Spanish or Norway timber came among us, which is likewise of a white colour." Quite possibly this imported timber was of Sessile oak.

Because of the variations in temperature and rainfall in the British Isles English oak shows unevenness of growth in the annual rings, (see Page 27) imported oak does not show these variations to such a marked degree. Oak grown in latitudes where the length of each growing season is less takes much longer to reach the same size as oak exposed to our maritime climate. As a consequence the grain of the timber is more compact. In the 17th Century imported oak was thought to have a more pronounced medullary ray, (see Page 21) which produced a better figure when cleft or quarter sawn. Be that as it may, it should be possible to identify imported oak in chests or boxes of the 17th century by the density of the annual rings; some have as many as thirty six rings to the inch, and it is difficult to imagine an English oak producing such timber however grown, particularly if this is apparent across a considerable width of board. Old oaks grown in isolation will produce such ring widths towards the end of their lives, but such timber would be difficult to cleave and some of the denser ring widths occur in cleft boards. (See the density of the annual rings in boxes 6 and 14, Page 29.) The timber found in 16th and 17th Century chests and boxes only came from three sources. From British woodlands, it was either coppice-grown or from wildwood trees; if imported it came from the ancient European or Scandinavian forests. Each source provided either cleft or sawn material. None of this came from planted trees, as does our modern oak, although the thinnings from Lord Burliegh's plantations might just have been of sufficient size by the 1650's.

Any regular slowing down or acceleration of growth will have been occasioned by the cutting of coppice among which the oak stood, in a coppice-with-standards system. Any timber produced by this system showing a seven to ten year rotation is likely to be early, and any showing ten to fifteen year intervals (and higher) should be late. In Hereford, fifteen year intervals were common in the mid-17th Century, and indeed are still employed to produce small-dimensioned material for farm use. Taking our period of study from 1550 to 1700, and assuming cleft oak to be no more than about 50 years old we are dealing with trees actually growing from 1500 to 1650, and the later longer rotations should apply. Home-grown timber should show wide variations in ring-widths.

With sawn timber, the same variations in ring widths should occur, the source of the timber being mainly the larger older trees from the remaining natural woodland, or from wood-pasture locations.

Sawn boards which display very narrow annual rings are more likely to have been imported; those with wider ring-widths should be from home-grown sources.

If we are correct in assuming that slow even growth with very narrow annual rings is more likely to have come from imported timber it is surprising to find in the timber analysis of the boxes that many of the early examples contain some timber from abroad in conjunction with home-grown timber from a coppice or open-grown source. One could understand this if the better quality timber had been used for the fronts or tops only, but use appears haphazard.

Where evidence of a coppice rotation exists in the timber it varies from five years to twenty-five years and is much more common in boxes made before about 1630. After that date, almost all the boxes contain oak which was open-grown. This timber was also more likely to have been sawn, perhaps because of the difficulty in cleaving large trees. Some of the later examples contain single panels up to 15" in width, particularly in the lids of desks. It is tempting to draw a conclusion from the data that the presence in a box of timber with very narrow annual rings indicates an early date; however, with such a small sample it would be unwise to do this without wider research.

Another interesting possibility lies in the presence in some of the boxes of timber showing, by narrower ring-widths, periods of drought. Single drought years are numerous in the period from 1540 to 1700, but there are only eight occasions between these years when three consecutive dry summers were recorded. These were 1539-1541, 1566-1568, 1590-1592, 1610-1612, 1614-1616, 1635-1637, 1651-1653, and 1684-1686.

Climatic records before the late 17th Century can only be gleaned from old reports, diaries, letters and so on, and at best are haphazard. The statement that a drought occurred in any particular year cannot be relied on, as there is no way of knowing how severe or long lasting the period of drought was or whether it would seriously affect tree growth. However, statements that "all the small rivers dried up", or that the Thames was so low that "even at the ebb tide sea water extended beyond London Bridge" could reasonably be held to have produced reduced growth in oak. In 1539-1541 these conditions occurred. Many cattle died from want of water, and such a subsequent lowering of the water-table must have affected the growth of trees. In 1566-1568 there was a group of moderately dry summers, but in 1590-1592, the Thames so dried up that a man could ride across it near London Bridge; such conditions must have been the result of considerable drought over the whole watershed of the river. In 1610-1612, the evidence is less, with a "great" drought recorded from January to May 1612; with a following wet summer this might not show significantly in a narrower tree ring. But in 1614-1616 droughts occurred from spring to late summer sufficient to cause scarcity in hay, corn, and grass; these years would surely show up in the timber. In 1635-1637 droughts were recorded during the summer and autumn of 1635 and from March to August 1636. In one of the summers of 1651-1653 John Evelyn (who as a Forester can be relied on) recorded "a drowth of nearly four months", and in 1684-1686 he mentions trees dying "for want of nourishment".

Taking such evidence as there is at its face value, it is necessary to assume that some of the recorded droughts would show up in the tree rings, but others not. The early 17th Century group of 1614-1616 which produced losses in crops sufficient to mention is more likely to have produced reduced tree growth than the period 1610-1612, which did not. Furthermore, if the dry years 1614-1616 do show up in a board, for them to be the only series of dry years to show up in the board, there should be a period of twenty-one years normal growth before they appeared (1592-1614) and eighteen years afterwards (1617-1635) a total of 42 years.

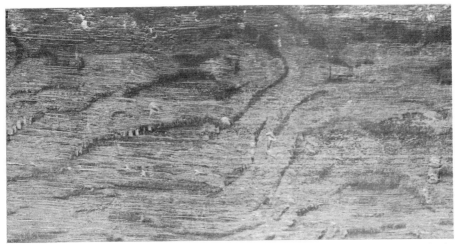

Medullary rays on the surface of an oak panel. These are specialised cells which the tree uses to store starch through its dormant period during the winter; they radiate like the spokes of a bicycle wheel from the centre of the tree to the inner bark and are only fully revealed when the log is cut "on the quarter" i.e. when each cut of the saw is approximately parallel to them. Such cutting is labour-intensive as each cut entails moving the log. Cleaving timber automatically reveals the rays as oak will only cleave radially and each board so produced exhibits the rays upon its surface. The rays give oak its characteristic "figure". Rays exist in other timbers, but not to such an extent as in oak.

One group of very marked dry years show up clearly on the back board of box no. 28. (See page 24). The concavity of the annual rings in this board show the direction of growth, which is from top to bottom in the photograph. The three dry rings occur about two inches up from the bottom of the board.

A further group of rings narrower than the average occurs about one and a half inches down from the top. Counting the rings between these two groups produces a period of twenty one years, or possibly between 1593 and 1614. There are sixteen rings after the lower group, unfortunately indistinct due to the saw-cuts.

From this, the newest ring in the board could have been laid down in 1632 and if we are correct in all our assumptions the box could not have been made before this date as the timber was still in the living tree. Just how far after that date the box was made is of course another matter. We believe that in the 1630's timber supplies were growing less and therefore more expensive, and it seems reasonable to assume that no workshop would hold stocks of sawn or cleft material for very long. Timber would probably be used as soon as it was seasoned, which with a board of 3/4" thickness would be in one year. Sapwood is usually present on about the outer two inches of the round log, and this was discarded as it was prone to insect attack and was not durable. Two inches of sapwood would take about twelve years to produce, bringing the earliest date for the box at 1644, plus the seasoning period. The style of the decoration, the shape of the lock plate and the scratch-block moulding on the cleft top all make this a likely date.

The backboard of box no. 30 also shows a single group of dry-summer rings, occurring seventeen years from the newest wood at the bottom of the photograph. Assuming again that these rings represent the summers of 1614-1616, the newest wood in the box was laid down in 1633. The rate of growth of the sapwood must have been much greater that than in box no. 14 at an estimated four rings to the inch, putting the earliest date for the box at about 1642. There are few clues as to date in the box itself; the simple (surely religious) "fish" motif indicates a Puritan origin as does its sturdy construction, the oak panels are all sawn, and five eighths of an inch thick. The best we can make of this is that it seems reasonable.

This line of enquiry is of course fraught with inaccuracies, depending as it does on so many assumptions. To be reasonable accurate, it would be necessary to know which part of the country the timber came from, and to have accurate meteorological data for that area.

Four of the boxes and one of the chests illustrated show prominent groups of three narrower consecutive annual rings, which leads us to the question as to why more boxes do not show the rings. The periods between drought groups vary between 13 years and 48 years; the maximum period of time during which a three ring series should occur is 68 years. This period of time would produce a board between six inches and ten inches in width; fairly common in the smaller table boxes.

Variations in ring width in coppice grown timber could well mask dry periods if these occurred when growth had already slowed as part of the coppice cycle, and about half of the boxes were made from coppice grown timber. Imported oak will not show English drought periods, and with such dense growth in imported timber, local variations would be difficult to detect. Similarly, with home grown oak from an open situation timber from the outer layers of an aged tree would not show differences apparent to the naked eye. Another possible cause of confusion is the likelihood that groups of narrower rings are not all from dry summers but are the result of the overcrowding of oaks just prior to the cutting of competing coppice regrowth. In the case of box no. 28 a twenty one year period between periods of slow growth is quite possible. However, the response of oak to the cutting of competing trees is usually not so marked as in this box, the trees normally take a year or two to resume their previous rate of growth. The immediately succeeding annual rings in both boxes 28 and 30 are quite large.

As I have indicated, the "dry-summer ring" theory is little more than this. However, there is one correlation with a dated box; this is the little Welsh box illustrated as box no. 52, dated 1716, it has a group of three narrower rings which correspond with the dry summers of 1704, 1705, and 1706.

....

It is worthwhile to consider here the size of the trees available to the the 16th and 17th Century workmen. Obviously the most favoured trees would be those which were more easily workable. Where the faster grown coppice oaks were available locally they would have been felled and processed first, and the most efficient way to do this would have been to have cleft or sawn the timber at stump. The converted material would be more easily removed than the logs. Within living memory, in Herefordshire cleft oak rails for gates were produced in the wood, where they were also stacked for seasoning for 12 months after cutting. There can be little doubt that pit-saws were employed within the wood; witness the number of woods still called "Sawpit Wood" today. I manage one within fifteen miles of Hereford, and there are many more.

At the end of the 16th Century, quite apart from the managed coppiced area there must still have been large areas of wood-pasture or wild

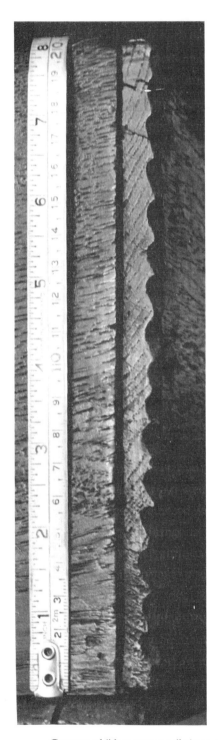

Groups of "dry-summer" rings on box no. 28, left, and box no. 30, right.

woodland containing trees of great size which had been avoided by the timber fallers of the day because of the difficulty of felling and conversion. Nowadays such trees are rare, but at one time they must have been prolific. The tree illustrated was blown down in the gales of 1990; with a diameter of over seven feet it would have been a formidable task to render it into 1" boards with a pit-saw. One can well imagine the felling gang of 1590 moving on to a more manageable log.

This tree was the "Crump Oak" which stood for nearly three hundred years beside the Hereford to Lyonshall road; I include it because examination of its annual rings gave me some confirmation of rates of growth for trees of this size growing in this locality. The tree may originally have been one of a group, but if this was so the trees within the group were well spaced to the point where they did not compete with each other. It was a short-boled pedunculate oak with a wide-spreading crown and apart from the usual variation in annual ring widths common to all home-grown oak, due to climatic factors, it shows a reasonably even rate of growth; in this it must mirror rates of growth of similar trees in the 16th Century.

For the first fifty years or so, it grew fairly rapidly, by 1770 it had settled down to a reasonably steady 5½ to 6 rings per inch.

The average rate of growth over 292 years was 7.12 rings to the inch across one radius of the tree and 7.72 across the opposite. The very slowest rate of growth was 16 rings to the inch over the sapwood, which was about two inches deep. Given that present day conditions were favourable to the growth of the tree, (and it was still a full-crowned specimen when it blew down) this latter rate of slow growth is interesting. I do not believe that growing conditions for oak were very different in the 16th Century, so if 16 rings to the inch is the slowest rate for a three hundred year old tree, where did the timber in the boxes come from which averages more than this? Ancient wild wood trees no doubt contained timber with narrower ring widths but they would have been avoided for the reasons earlier stated.

Box no. 11 almost certainly was made in Herefordshire, and the rates of growth of the oak from which it was made tally very closely with that in this tree. The front panel of the box grew at about 18 rings to the inch, the back panel (which was probably from a coppice-grown tree) averaged between 6 and 7 rings to the inch. Other present-day fellings of locally grown oak are coming up with similar average rates of growth.

Individual narrow annual rings in the Crump Oak sections tie in very closely with dry summers which are recorded, from the recent 1976 right back to 1730. One swallow does not make a summer, and one tree does not prove a theory, but there is much of interest in the Crump Oak data.

Nevertheless I regret the passing of such a fine tree; I drove past it for thirty years. When it blew down it contained over a thousand cubic feet (Hoppus measure) of millable timber in the trunk and limbs; when mature it inhabited about a quarter acre of land.

It is difficult to obtain information on rates of growth at different locations in the United Kingdom. Private estates, if they keep records at all, simply record volumes of timber per compartment; occasionally valuations involving measurement of timber are made for Probate or other purposes but these are almost entirely concerned with capital values. Better managed estates do record sample plot data mainly to assess productivity, there is no reason to record rates of growth expressed in annual rings per inch. Timber merchants are solely interested in the quality of the end product.

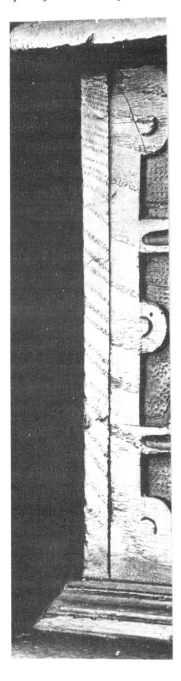

End-grain on the back panel of box no. 16. The tree took thirty-five years to make this piece of timber. Note the slowing down of growth in the last ten years at the top of the panel. With such fast growth at the bottom, the tree was probably coppice-grown. As the growth of the cut coppice increased, root competition denied the oak sufficient nutrients and moisture to sustain the early rapid growth, resulting in narrower ring-widths at the top.

Evidence of the coppice origin of the oak in box no. 21. Growth from bottom to top. After a period of fast growth, there are 4 years of restricted growth, followed by 14 years fast growth; then 5 years restricted, 8 years fast, and five years restricted. Note the suddenness of increases and decreases of growth on each side of the narrow ring areas.

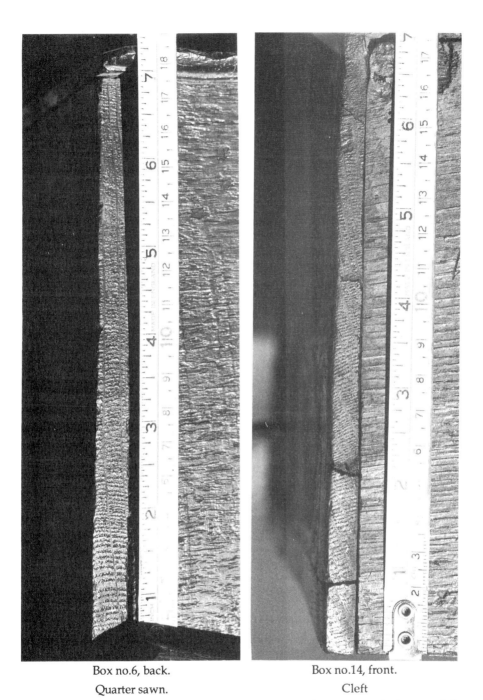

Box no.6, back.   Box no.14, front.

Quarter sawn.   Cleft

The timber from which these boards were made was almost certainly imported; in British timber ring widths of these densities will only occur in the outer few inches of wood in elderly trees, these are over 7½" width of board.

Coppice-grown oak, Herefordshire. Wall Hills, near Ledbury.
The short lengths of knot-free timber and wide spreading crowns are typical of trees grown under this ancient system. Such fast-grown timber cleaves very easily. These trees are 40-50 years old and have seen perhaps three cuttings of competing regrowth, the last in 1989.

The Forestry Commission is mainly concerned with coniferous forests but they do assess yields of timber throughout their woodlands, and have sample plot data for hardwoods too, although these account for only about six percent of their woodland areas. Nevertheless, their figures are interesting.

The following are based on subcompartment measurements taken in Forestry Commission woodlands in 1970; they express the production potential of sites as a figure representing the total annual increase in volume in cubic meters on one hectare in one year. In United Kingdom woodlands, the range for oak lies roughly between three cubic meters per hectare and five; in the (now superseded) Forestry Commission Conservancy areas the mean yields were as follows:

North Wales	3.88	(107)
East	3.93	(109)
North East	4.01	(111)
North West	4.17	(115)
South East	4.25	(118)
South West	4.35	(121)
South Wales	4.82	(134)

(Forestry Occasional Paper no. 12, P.H. Nicholls, Forestry Commission 1981)

For better comparison I have converted cubic meters (which I do not like) into cubic feet (Hoppus) in brackets; there is obviously considerable variation across the six Conservancy areas. However, any attempt to relate these figures to annual rainfall falls down immediately when one compares the first two areas, the rainfall in parts of North Wales is probably twice that in the East. Unless the North Wales data came from one single sample plot on a barren infertile site, other factors must apply, and one must look to altitude and soil type.

Professor Mark Anderson, in his *Selection of Tree Species,*[*] classifies the natural woodlands of the British Isles into fifteen communities of which four are of interest to our present study as they are associated with the production of oak. They are:

1. "The Ash-Oakwood community. This is an important and widespread community occurring on soils of intermediate fertility with moderate moisture content. It is definitely a lowland community which at one time must have covered wide areas of the more fertile drift soils of central England and Ireland as well as the clays and marls of Somerset, Hampshire, Dorset, Devon, and Oxfordshire. It also occurs however in narrow bands along the valley- bottoms of the Silurian limestone hills of Hereford and in the Carboniferous limestone areas of Yorkshire and Northumberland, in considerable areas on the Silurian Slates of Westmorland and Cumberland................the community is closely allied to the Moist Oakwood community, into which it gradually merges. Ash and Oak are the predominant trees." (Ash, Oak, and Hazel are still found in close association today on what were once coppiced areas.)

2. "The Moist Oakwood Association. In point of area covered, this was probably the predominant British forest association............. There are certainly several types of this important association. In the climatically drier areas of the east and south it is confined to the moister loams and stiffer clays, such as are found over the London Clay, Gault and Weald Clay in Kent, Sussex and elsewhere and on the Oxford Clay............The association would appear to have occupied the valley-bottoms of the Silurian hills of Wales.

3. The Dry Oakwood Communities. Gradations occur between these

---

[*]   Published 1961 by Oliver & Boyd.

communities and the last-named association. They occur on drier more porous soils with relatively low fertility and are found on sandy soils from Hampshire round the south-east and east coast.......

4.   The Oak-Birch Community. Extensive areas of light sandy soils are found in the south-east of England in Kent, Surrey and Sussex, also near Bedford and further north in Cheshire and Nottinghamshire .... These sandy areas, which in the Midlands of England and possibly further south mark the location of the terminal moraine of one of the most important ice-sheets of the glacial epoch, are somewhat infertile but not extremely so......... when cleared of woodland the soil tends to deteriorate rapidly and the vegetation develops into poor heath . . ."

Obviously the more suitable the site for Oak the faster it will grow, and coppice-grown trees in the first two communities above will show quicker increment than trees produced on the drier areas. Moreover, coppice rotations will be shorter. The same is true of the wood-pasture and wildwood trees growing under similar conditions.

On the drier sites, Oak will still be produced as standard trees over coppice regrowth, but more slowly. The larger trees growing in isolation however, in addition to slower growth, will be very liable to defects; principally ring-shake, which can render the timber useless for constructional purposes. This is a very common defect of Oak on drier sites.

The present-day rainfall and regional climates in this country cannot differ greatly from those of the 16th and 17th Centuries. Across the southern half of the country the areas of lowest annual rainfall generally coincide with those areas where this occurs in the second half of the year, when oak trees have more or less completed their annual growth. The maximum period of growth within a tree ring lies in the spring wood, where vessels of large diameter are able to transport sap more rapidly. In the areas of higher rainfall, most of this falls during the winter; here, spring droughts need not adversely affect growth of the trees, as moisture will be available in the water-table which has been replenished during the winter. The fastest rate of growth should therefore be expected in areas with between 7 and 9 months of growing season, and rainfall above 30".

Conversely, the slowest rate of growth should appear in those areas of five or six months of growing season, and a rainfall of less than 30".

The range of maximum ring-widths in the illustrated chests and boxes is from 4 to 12, with the widths at the fastest-growing end of the scale occurring in Devon, Somerset, and Wales, in Hereford and the Welsh border counties this drops to 6 or 7 to the inch, in line with those in the Crump oak. In the table on pages 67/68 I have no provenance for any of the boxes from 8 to 10 rings to the inch; but I suggest that they are very likely to have come from Professor Anderson's "Dry Oakwood" or "Oak-Birch" communities. (This is of course a fair guess as they cover a considerable area. Some correlation with carving styles in these areas would be helpful.)

The very fast rate of growth in the two welsh boxes (nos 40 and 41) is interesting, it equates well with the present-day Forestry Commission sample plot figures for this region.

TOOLS

The human race has been fortunate in inhabiting a planet with a self-replenishing natural resource which in its natural state is almost ready to use. Initially, only a very few crude tools were necessary to fell the tree and shape the timber; the same axe that felled the tree could also be used to split it longitudinally thus increasing the amount of useful material. Further splitting of the timber radially could produce boards of tapered section. This method of converting round timber into useable material was very quick, and entailed the expenditure of minimum effort; it also saved the considerable effort of moving the felled tree as it was far easier simply to move the converted material from the felling area. Not all home-grown timber splits easily, but straight grained oak is perhaps the best; our ancestors must very quickly have determined this.

Once the shape of the axe head had been established, there was very little room for improvement in the tool; the modern felling axe is very similar to its ancient forebears. Indeed, the only improvement in perhaps 10,000 years was the introduction of the socket into the head in Bronze Age Europe; previously the head had been simply tied into a cleft in the handle. Iron Age, Roman, and Medieval axes were virtually identical in shape, being identical in purpose.

A logical development of the axe was the adze, which is simply the former with the blade placed for convenience in a different plane. It must have been invented after the introduction of a socketed head; it is difficult to see how it could have been attached to a cleft stick in the earlier fashion. The two tools must have been worked side by side, particularly in early shipbuilding. Some shipbuilding timbers needed to be shaped to a square section, but others, particularly in the ribs, had to be curved, and for this purpose the adze was ideal. Such use was described in the "Odyssey". Such a crude tool, in skilled hands, could produce remarkably good surfaces; without it the great Cathedrals of the Middle Ages could not have been built; it was the correct shape to produce the curved braces that formed a vital part of the roof timbers, and could quickly produce a reasonably flat surface on a beam. I believe it may have been quicker to square a round log into a beam with an adze than a pit saw.

The concept of the adze must surely have led to that of the plane, in which the metal blade is presented to the surface of the timber in the same way, but made to produce a more uniform flat surface by virtue of the surrounding (and supporting) block of wood. Again, once the basic arrangement had been arrived at there was little room for improvement; planes from the time of the Romans to the 18th Century were not appreciably different. A further development of the plane was the spoke-shave, which is such a useful tool that it is still in use today.

One of the earliest hand tools with a straight cutting edge must have been the chisel, with it for the first time it became possible to excavate square holes in timber, enabling joints to be made. Some joints are of great antiquity; there are dove-tailed drawers in boxes from the tomb of Tutankhamun.

The straight chisel was only useful in producing in producing flat cuts, when surface decoration became necessary it developed into the gouge, with a curved cross section, or the "V" tool, which could dig channels in the timber. When one considers the range of wood-carving tools available to the medieval craftsman it is not surprising that they produced work of astonishing quality. Given the soft nature of the metal from which such tools were made however they must have worn quickly, resharpening must have been frequent.

Saws are probably the only cutting tools which could not evolve further until metal working techniques improved. The earliest saws cut in one direction only, as they were pulled towards the operator; a "push" stroke would have buckled the blade. This relatively inefficient method of cutting had to prevail until the 18th Century, when it became possible by the use of water power to make blades of rolled steel. Saws for felling and ripping until then were equally inefficient, the "sharks tooth" shape of the teeth led to clogging of the cut with sawdust. The concept of a subsidiary raking tooth seems to have escaped invention until the 19th

Century. The "setting" of saw teeth was understood very early on, Pliny describes the process accurately. Each tooth was bent slightly outwards, alternating to left or right along the length of the blade. This resulted in the thickness of the cut being slightly greater than the width of the metal from which the blade was made, making it easier to pull through the timber and less liable to clog. The "kerf" or width of the cut was surprisingly wide. The ornamental saw cuts in box no. 1 are far wider than those which a modern bow saw would have produced.

The use of thin saw blades gave rise to the necessity of tensioning them in some way, this was achieved from earliest times by the use of a frame, the tension being applied through leverage using a "spanish windlass" to produce the tension. Similar saws are still in use today in undeveloped countries.

All the hand tools in daily use in the 16th and 17th Centuries were virtually identical with those known to much earlier civilisations. It is interesting to compare the various tools illustrated in figures 1 and 2. The former comes from a book published on the Continent in 1574 showing chest makers at work, the latter is from a fragment of Roman glass.

Between 2000 and 3000 B.C., Egyptian carpenters used hand tools made from bronze, which being an alloy of copper and tin produced a tool with a better cutting edge than those made solely of copper. Axes, adzes, chisels and saws were all in use and Egyptian woodworking practices advanced to such a degree that all the common methods of joining wood together were known to them.

By the time of the 16th and 17th Century box makers, any evolution in the shape or function of tools had already occurred, the properties of timber and techniques for working it were long established.

In England from Anglo Saxon times, carpentry was possibly the most important craft furnishing most of the things necessary to everyday life, from buildings to wooden plates. Very few early tools have survived; perhaps because they wore out so quickly, but they were greatly prized; their frequent mention in wills is an indication of their importance. In the days before the Dissolution of the Monasteries, tools were probably the property of the Church, and provided by the workshop, but afterwards, when the workmen had dispersed to work on secular buildings and furniture in the late Tudor period they no doubt provided their own.

After such a long period when woodworking techniques and tools had remained unchanged, the late 16th Century craftsmen must have been utterly familiar with their trade, which is reflected in the fine quality of the wooden buildings and furniture which still exist today. When the Renaissance brought new forms of decoration, these were simply grafted on to existing methods of woodworking and quietly absorbed by the craftsmen. No new tools were necessary, they simply carried on with those which were already to hand.

In contrast to some of the early ecclesiastical woodwork, the simple construction of chests and boxes made few demands on the craftsmen. They needed to know how to measure, and to make right-angled cuts. Right angles were marked with a set square, one is prominently displayed on the bench in figure 1. Sawn timber would come to them already of the correct thickness; cleft panels may well have been provided still as they emerged from the cleaving process, with a thin wedge-shaped cross section; this would be worked into a uniform thickness with a plane or more probably a spokeshave, which is ideal for the purpose. The complete lack of uniformity in the measurements of the timber in the early boxes leads me to conclude that they used whatever timber came to hand and squared off the ends accordingly; random thicknesses occur in many of these boxes, particularly when made from cleft material.

The simplest joint was made by "butting" two pieces of timber together and nailing one to the other, usually the front panel overlaps the sides. (see page 43) All that was needed to produce a satisfactory box was to ensure that all the pieces of wood had right-angled ends. A stronger joint was made by "rebating"; here the box did not depend merely on nails to provide rigidity; lateral movement of the end panels was prevented by the shoulders on the inside of the front panel. To make the joint, all that was required was the use of a saw and a chisel. The "dovetail" was a far more complex joint, which is probably why so few boxes have them. It seems not to have become common until the late 17th Century, when a great deal of furniture making had passed to the joiners who were more skilled.

Fig. 1.

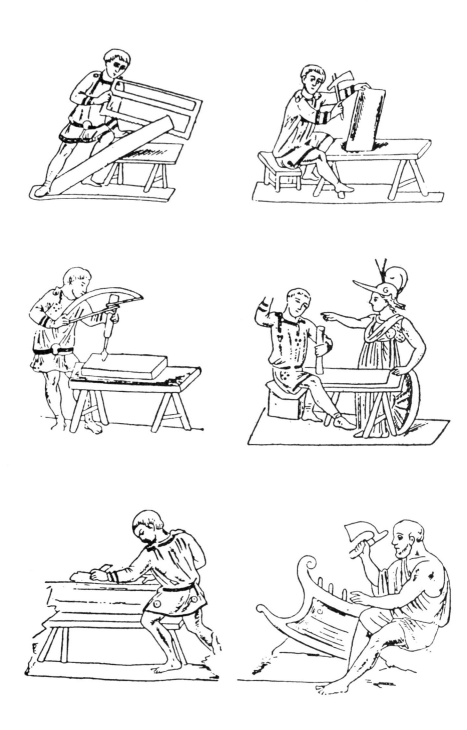

Fig. 2.

The surface of the boards used to make the boxes was usually finished by planing; the tool marks can very often be seen on the timber. The workmen ground off the edges of plane blades to prevent the formation of ridges at the sides of each cut, producing very shallow concave cuts in the surface which are visible if viewed from an angle. It is a tribute to their skill with the plane that a satisfactory surface could be produced with this tool alone. Where surfaces present a flat uniform appearance, this must have been achieved by scraping, either with a flat piece of metal, or even by glass.

Embellishment of boxes by carving was usually left to the carver, although undoubtedly some makers did attempt their own decoration, usually with poor results. Some country boxes with crude carving do have a certain appeal, but they cannot stand comparison with the crisp, highly competent work produced by skilled carvers, who were always a separate trade. There is some evidence from the boxes that the makers would send panels to the carvers; front and back panels with identical ring widths do occur but this could be coincidental. It is more likely that the carvers bought their timber direct from the suppliers, whether of imported or home grown material. For carving, timber needs to be easily workable, and thus free of knots. Imported oak with narrow ring widths would work more easily than home grown timber which has considerable variation in the density of each annual ring. The early spring growth in home grown oak is usually soft and fairly constant in width, but in a broad ring the extra width is made up of the harder denser summer growth; such timber is more difficult to carve satisfactorily than the timber with more even narrower rings. For particularly fine work the latter is essential and I feel that the carvers would have preferred to choose their own material rather than rely on that sent by the box makers.

Evidence from the boxes suggests that although a wide range of carving tools was available, only very few were actually used. Close examination of the enlarged detail in the photographs makes this clear. Usually, a deep "V" tool was used to outline the design on the board, supplemented by only two or three gouges of different size with a shallow concave section which excavated the deeper parts of the design. In later, and some country boxes, only the "V" tool was used. The early carvers also further embellished their designs with a whole range of punches, which were easily made by filing the ends of metal bars. These made a wide range of impressions ranging from zig-zag lines to stars, and included square or oblong punches which served to matt the background to the work

Given such a narrow range of tools, the richness and vitality of much of the carving is surprising. I believe that contrary to what one might expect, a skilled carver could work at quite a speed, and no doubt had to. There is a strength of line in the good carving which shows the complete confidence of the craftsman.

Perhaps this is not so surprising if one considers that behind a lifetime of experience with the tools was a seven year apprenticeship, and behind that was a tradition spreading back over several millenia.

Dovetailed

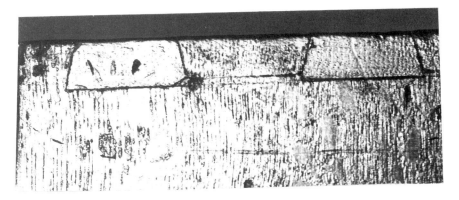

Rebated

Butted

THE MAKERS

In the Middle Ages, during the period when most woodwork was sponsored by the Church, there were two groups of craftsmen. The first, the carpenters, were highly skilled and were mainly responsible for structural woodwork, some of which was of great complexity. The second group were the Hutchiers whose main function was to produce planked furniture such as tables and chests. The old name for a six-plank chest was "ark", hence Arkwright, the alternative name for the hutchier.

After the Dissolution of the Monasteries, when the craftsmen had dispersed to work on the houses and furniture of the newly rich. the two trades merged. The newer, lighter methods of construction demanded skilled techniques; the use of the mortice and tenon joint became widespread in the framework of the panelled furniture of the period (the use of panels within a supporting framework helped to prevent the warping and splitting of the timber which had long been a problem in planked furniture).

What today are called demarcation disputes became common between the less skilled craftsmen and the joiners, and to regularise matters the Guild of Joiners was formed in London in 1632. Like all the Guilds of the period, its prime purpose was to protect the livelihood of its members by excluding non-members from the local trades, and to prevent competition from foreign craftsmen. In the late 16th and 17th Centuries, these were principally the Flemish craftsmen who had a similar long tradition of working in oak. The reluctance of the Guild to accept foreign influences may have led to the moribund nature of the style of English furniture during this period.

The more benign influence of the Guild lay in the form of quality control which it exercised, and the high standards of workmanship which ensued from the apprenticeship system, which demanded that a pupil should serve seven years beneath a master craftsman, and be admitted to the

Guild not later than the age of twenty-four.

In such a restricted, exclusive environment innovation in furniture making and design was unlikely, and new ideas had to wait until the Restoration in 1660 when Continental fashions flowed into England with the return of Charles II. Perhaps coincidentally, following the great fire of London in the same year, new forms of furniture such as the gate-leg table and the chest of drawers became popular, and from about this date onwards, fashion dictated that the old styles were gradually superseded. The joiners became cabinet makers, and box making became more and more a provincial craft.

In London, the box makers had been a subsidiary of the Joiners Guild for only some thirty years and the second half of the century saw a general decline in workmanship as box making became more and more of a rural industry, with an absence of the discipline under which the old craftsmen worked.

By the 18th Century, competition from the new cabinet makers and from exotic imported woods such as the mahoganies drove the trade into further oblivion. There was still a demand for small lockable boxes which lingered on into Victorian times, but these were seldom decorated. By the 18th Century, the "mule" chest and the chest of drawers had made the larger six-plank chests obsolete too.

The peak years for box making were probably between 1600 and 1650; certainly most exant boxes appear to be of this period. (Although at times I wonder whether we are too nervous about ascribing earlier dates to boxes, certainly the middle-class prosperity in the later years of Elizabeth's reign would seem unrepresented in the quantity of boxes allotted to pre-1600.)

It must be accepted that the skill required by the actual maker of the boxes was minimal; indeed it is surprising that a seven year apprenticeship was needed. What probably sold the box was the quality of the carving. As a separate trade, carvers could set themselves up wherever a sufficiently large and prosperous population existed. Outside London, there were very few centres of population where they could prosper, and in the second half of the 17th Century there was plenty of

Fig. 3.

work for them, and they had no need to retreat as did the box makers to the more remote market towns. Towards the end of the century, the provincial box maker must have found it increasingly difficult to find a local carver sufficiently skilled to embellish his boxes; certainly the quality of the carving on some of the later boxes bears this out. Deep gouge work in the 18th Century was kept to a minimum, and the quicker "V" tool was employed more extensively than hitherto. There is little skill involved in using this, and the profuse use of this tool in later work probably indicates that the box makers themselves employed it, with greater or less effect. (See figure 4 "The box maker carveth them with a knife")

The scale of the decline in workmanship is apparent if one compares the carving on box no. 43 dated 1719 with that on any of the early 17th Century boxes.

That such a box could sell at all is a reflection on the standards of the buyer, admittedly, but it also epitomises the collapse of what must have been a thriving trade.

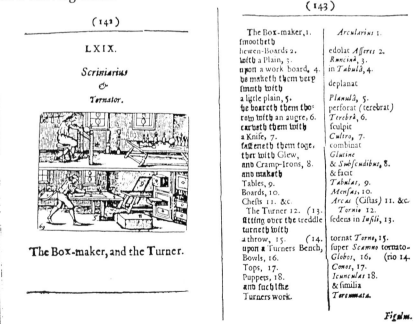

Fig. 4.

A page from *Orbis Sensualium Pictus* by Johan Amos Comenius. 1659

THE BOXES

J.P. Blake, in "Little Books about Old Furniture" published in 1911 claims that "Bible" boxes were a little larger than their seventeenth or eighteenth century Bibles "which they were made to contain". He was certainly right about the size; I have measured two early 17th Century Bibles and they were 17" by 12" by 6½" and 16" by 12" by 4", any of the illustrated boxes could have contained them. The idea that the boxes had been made for this purpose arose in Victorian times, but there are no contemporary records that they were thus used at the time when they were made. Undoubtedly they were an ideal size in which to keep the Victorian family Bible and without doubt were used in this way, but the idea that they were made for this purpose must be put down to Victorian romanticism.

Very few boxes appear to have religious motifs, indeed the very opposite is true, most of the commonly used designs in the carving have a distinctly pagan origin, which their original owners well knew, and it is possible that devout worshippers would have regarded such use as blasphemous.

It is significant that the emergence of these little boxes as useful articles of furniture coincided with the growing prosperity of the merchant class in the later Tudor years; we should perhaps regard them as the possessions of the upper middle classes of this period. The growing prosperity of farmers and artisans during the years of James 1st created a further market and there is evidence of this in the numbers of "middle period" boxes, say from 1620 to 1650, which still survive today.

As to the use to which they were put, I think it likely that we can regard the larger six plank chests as masculine articles of furniture and the smaller table boxes as feminine. Certainly, jewellery and cash would have been kept in the little boxes, as they were lockable, and the tills present in some of the boxes must have been put there for this purpose. They would have also been useful for the storage of small accessories to dress,

Figure 2:161. *Wrought iron strap-hinge (from the spice chest in Figure 3:298). English, c.1670. Note the pitted and polished surface which is typical of iron fittings of this age. The hinge is held in place with three hand-made nails, and the lack of marks in the surrounding wood suggests that it has not been moved or altered.*

up drye with stikks betweene it so that it may season the better''. He was much concerned that his timbers should be well-prepared, and only three days previously he had instructed his steward to be sure that ''there be plancks sawen for my dores so that they may be seasoned in tyme''. Like most patrons of his time, Thynne held his craftsmen responsible for the quality of the material they used, and he wrote of his joiners that if he should ''finde any faut with the workmanship or the seasoning of their stuf...

modern times.

Hardware

One supply which no joiner or carpenter could manage without, was that of metal hardware and nails. Even though it is not desirable to use iron nails in the *construction* of oak furniture, it is impossible to avoid the use of locks, handles and hinges on almost every sort of chest, box, cupboard and folding table; and such hardware is always fixed with iron nails.

The huge variety of iron fittings were made and supplied, wrought on the anvil, by blacksmiths. There is also a good deal of evidence that furniture fittings were supplied by whitesmiths, with a bright tinned finish. This polished finish has almost always worn off, but where it does remain (e.g. inside chests or cupboards), the corroded layer of tin shows up clearly as a thin grey layer, like a coat of grey paint. Where original iron fittings are present, their condition should reflect the state of the surrounding wood. On patinated surfaces, the iron will be a rich glossy black, usually surrounded by a black patch of acid stain in the wood. On dry inside surfaces, the iron may be pale and dry, or lightly tinged with rust. Where the wood is heavily worn and weathered, the iron will be corroded and pitted with rust. Hinges and other moving parts will often have a light powdering of rust around the pivot barrel.

The presence of original ironwork on furniture is always interesting and important. Quite often, of course, iron fittings have had to be replaced because of past wear or breakage. There exists a bill of 1760 from Eliakim Smith (a joiner of Hadley, Connecticut), to one John Eastman, for making

45. Ibid.
46. Ibid.

hairdressing items, and cosmetics. Smaller items of wearing apparel such as gloves and handkerchiefs would certainly have found their way into the boxes; two of the illustrated boxes are lined with paper bearing the Arms of the Haberdashers Guild. Small hand mirrors were greatly prized in the 16th and 17th Centuries. The first English glass mirrors were produced by Sir Robert Mansell in 1618; prior to this they had been made of polished speculum and were very expensive; they would surely have been kept under lock and key. Pomanders, used to ward off infection when travelling, would also need to be kept covered when not in use, lest the spices which they contained lost their strength. Hair dyes, wigs, and ruffs (which needed to be stored away from dust) would also have been stored in the boxes. (At any rate up to about the 1630's, when ruffs went out of fashion.)

In keeping with the flamboyant nature of the times, ladies of the late 16th and early 17th Centuries owned large quantities of jewellery. The men might have found the boxes useful for neck-chains, hat badges, signet rings and ceremonial daggers, but their wives would have used them for chains, collars, necklaces, ear-rings, pearls, brooches, buttons, fans, and all sorts of minor accessories.

Small domestic items such as scissors and needles must also have had to be kept secure; needlework and embroidery materials (some of which were of precious metals) were expensive. Embroidery was so extensively employed to decorate articles of of clothing and furnishing that it must have occupied the ladies of the period for many hours of the day; embroidery patterns of the time share so many motifs with the carved front panels of the boxes that there must be a connection.

The use of table boxes to contain cosmetics probably died out with the Restoration; "dressing" tables make their appearance about that time, and the introduction of the chest of drawers must have usurped many of the functions of the table boxes in that things could at last be stored separately. Perhaps at this time the boxes moved from the bedroom to the hall where they could still usefully contain items such as gloves and bonnets. (However, the term "Bonnet drawer" was used for some time to describe the deeper bottom drawers in chests of drawers.)

Inventories of wills in the early 17th Century mention small boxes frequently; their value ranged from sixpence to three shillings.

(They are mentioned so frequently that I wonder again whether many of the boxes which remain with us today are earlier than we think.)

The larger six plank chests must have served their original owners as something between the modern safe and filing cabinet. Paper, ink and pens would have surely lived in the little desks of the period, but the bigger boxes must have served to preserve business records, deeds and so on.

Today we give the term "Deed-box" to any small lockable narrow box which does not seem to have had any other purpose, but the documents comprising early deeds could be quite large, particularly if maps were included.

By the 16th Century, map making had reached a high degree of accuracy. After the discovery of the principle of triangulation (by Frisius in 1533) the making of accurate maps became common, and as the accurate fixing of boundaries was at last possible, maps would have been of considerable importance to the landowners of the time. It is certain that such maps would have been carefully preserved, and rolled up under lock and key, the six plank chest was the ideal place in which to store them. As deeds go hand-in-hand with maps, it seems reasonable to assume that they too would have inhabited the larger chests. Indeed, I know of two Herefordshire Estates today where maps and records are still stored in chests.

As fashions in furniture changed, the clumsy heavy chests were gradually abandoned in fashionable households and moved further down the social scale. There always has been a use for a sturdy box, if only to keep logs in, and being virtually indestructible the six plank chests have come down to us in considerable numbers.

Ironically, from being the poor relation of the more ornate panelled coffers, the six plank chests are on their way back up the social ladder again. A recent article in a magazine devoted to "decor" has urged its readers that the smart thing to do is to have one at the end of the bed. Which is of course where most of them originally sat.

DATING

It is virtually impossible to accurately date chests and boxes from the type of decoration which they display. Provincial craftsmen used motifs for years after they had gone out of fashion in the cities; popular designs were repeated over many decades out of habit or nostalgia, and no doubt plain boxes were decorated for one reason or another years after they had been made.

When dates do appear on boxes they are a useful guide to the decorative styles which were in use at the time, but dates and initials were very often a later addition. This can usually be detected by the awkward look of the inserted date compared with the design as a whole, plus perhaps the obvious use of a different tool. (See box no. 54.)

Many boxes may have been carved with older motifs simply to "go" with decoration on existing furniture already in the possession of the owner.

The "new" decorations that came into England during the reigns of Henry VIII and Elizabeth, and which within a generation or two were to completely supplant the Gothic, had already travelled far. The late Elizabethan beds and court cupboards became encrusted with designs that had been proceeding northwards from the Mediterranean countries for millenia, moving from country to country, sometimes pausing, but hardly evolving once the basic design had established itself.

The oldest was perhaps the simple "S" scroll (see the lower part of the front panel of box no. 29). This probably originated in Ancient Egypt, where it appeared as a simple ornament derived from a plant-stem. It spread through all the Arab countries of the Mediterranean and thence to Greece and Rome. Through the "Dark Ages" it appears to pause, and then move via the Renaissance from Venice to northern Europe, and finally into England.

Acanthus Plant form.

Greek Acanthus scroll.

Acanthus scroll derivative.

Fig. 5.

52

Part of this plant stem/"S" curve floral motif is repeated on the front panel of box no.6. Embroidery motifs occuring on many boxes probably indicate one of their uses. Design for embroidery by Thomas Trevelyon, beginning of the 17th c. From a MS book, early 17th c, in the Folger Shakespeare Library, Washington, U.S.A.

Fig. 6.

The nulling on the front panel of box no.9 closely resembles that on the border of this Corinthian cup of the 5th Century BC. (Martin von Wagner Museum, Wurzburg.)

Guilloche decoration around this bowl of about 580 BC occurs around a rose motif in box no.5. (National Archaeological Museum, Athens.)

One reason for its longevity as a decorative device is, I believe, because it is easy to make; the human hand has always been more adept at producing curves as it can pivot from wrist or elbow; also, given a square or oblong space to fill, the "S" curve can do this in a way which is satisfying to the eye as the empty spaces in the design balance each other perfectly. Strapwork (see Boxes no.16 and 34) is constructed of "S" curves, and was used with great enthusiasm as a decorative form on buildings of the period, moving almost simultaneously onto furniture. Strapwork had a definite "Arabesque" origin, which reappeared in Venice during the 16th

Century. During this century, Venice had become a well established market for Islamic wares and motifs from Damascened brassware appeared at the same time as the rediscovery of the artwork of the Romans, giving rise to the style of decoration known as "Grotesque", from the grottos in which the remains of the old designs were found.

There is also the possibility that an alternative source for strapwork lies in the iron-bound chests of German origin of an earlier date, the strapwork patterns imitate the iron bands.

Italian artists began to use these "new" styles in about 1530, whilst in England, Italian artists under the patronage of the Court and the nobility were soon using the new decorations to replace the more severe forms of the late Gothic period. There is a parallel in the 20th Century when Italian designers caused a similar revolution in the design of clothes and cars.

Towards the end of the 16th Century, the influence upon design had changed, partly for religious and political reasons, from the Catholic Italian to the Protestant Flemish, and a florid interpretation of Renaissance designs invaded the country, lasting virtually through the whole of the reign of James 1st.

Flemish furniture had been imported since the 15th Century and the publication of books such as "Architectural" by Johams de Vries in 1577 disseminated patterns which English craftsmen adopted with vigour. The lighter framed and panelled furniture of the late Elizabethan and early Jacobean periods became emblazoned with flower and fruit motifs, together with lunettes, strapwork, lozenges, masks and grotesques, all of Mediterranean origin. (The vine and grape motif was particularly popular.)

The only element of design in all this which could be held to be English is the formal, stylised English rose which appears on much of the furniture of the period. Although this must undoubtedly be the Tudor rose, even here such floral decoration can be traced right back to a desert origin; it appears time and again in Islamic artwork.

Lunette decoration is sometimes Anglicised with the insertion of a half-rose in place of the more usual Mediterranean acanthus or palm leaf designs.

It is easy to understand how the exotic designs from the South should find such an enthusiastic reception in the austere England of the late Tudor period, the severe Gothic styles had lingered for perhaps too long and they were certainly no longer in keeping with the spirit of the age, which was one of enterprise and energy. Once established, the new motifs became employed in a most haphazard way, and were to be so employed for virtually the whole of the first half of the 17th Century until the years of the Commonwealth, when decoration was discouraged and there was a pause until the Restoration.

Once again, the European influence was to assert itself; Charles II brought back with him a Flemish style of decoration which was soon to oust the old "English" designs. The tulip appears on boxes, perhaps as a political statement in line with the use of the Tudor rose in earlier years, or perhaps as a result of the mania which had developed surrounding the plant. This was to linger into the 18th Century as a design on table boxes, sometimes in conjunction with a vase motif the Greek origin of which by then would have been forgotten.

The buyer of a box in the late 16th Century was a completely different person from his late 17th Century counterpart. His education and outlook were wholly governed by Classicism and the decoration of his furniture reflected this. The discoveries to come as the 17th Century progressed were to completely change the attitudes of the educated people to the world around them, particularly with regard to symbolism, and thus to decoration.

It is almost impossible to get into the minds of the pre-Gallilean people of the late 16th Century; our understanding is so overlaid by what has happened since. Despite the power of religious thought they had a firm belief in the powers of the moon, the planets and the stars to influence their daily lives; each of these bodies had its own plants, animals, and minerals. Modern astrology is a trivial hobby compared to the way in which it was practised then. Physicians routinely employed astrology to diagnose and treat illness of every description; people firmly believed that there was an association between various signs of the Zodiac and different parts of the human anatomy.

Despite the considerable fund of knowledge about indigenous plants and animals people sincerely believed in bizarre mythical creatures such as the phoenix, the mermaid, and the unicorn. In 1616, despite all the voyages of discovery Godfrey Goodman in "The Fall of Man" held that man's ability to cross the Tropics would lead to the end of the world as this was evidence of the degradation of the human race.

There was an underlying understanding that the world was composed of irresistible forces that man was forced to obey. This was derived from the Graeco/Roman view of the universe as one of harmony between man and nature.

Running parallel with all this was a new developing awareness of a different universe; in 1609 Gallileo made a telescope and observed the landscape of the moon. Previously this had been held to be a perfect sphere of crystal, suddenly it was seen to have mountains and valleys. A year later, when Gallileo observed the planets of Jupiter, he was not believed; it was held that because Aristotle had not mentioned the satellites of Jupiter they could not exist. Perceiving the danger in all this, in 1616 the Church declared heretical the theory that the sun, and not the earth, was the centre of the universe.

However, the tide of superstition was beginning to ebb; in 1608 the decimal system was published in England, in 1614 John Napier inverted logarithms. In 1606, Francis Bacon wrote his "Advancement of Learning"; this new, mechanistic view of the world and its problems was to lead directly to the formation of the Royal Society. In 1665 it published "Philosophical Transactions", one of the first scientific periodicals. In 1687 Newton published his "Mathematical Principles of Natural Philosophy".

For the educated person of the late 17th Century the old world of the spirit had disappeared; the Renaissance universe had been replaced by one of geometric patterns, devoid of magic. Everything, it now seemed, could be explained by scientific investigation.

On the boxes, the early first period designs based on the classical motifs of lozenges, lunettes, acanthus and vine leaves all disappeared, to be replaced by more geometric patterns such as roundels and scrolls; carving became shallower and cruder and devoid of character.

This change in style of course was not abrupt; fashions changed slowly in the 17th Century, but there appears to be a time about the middle of the century where the classical motifs die out. In some regions they lingered longer than in others; strapwork appears on north country furniture into the 1680's, and I have seen a box so decorated with the date 1720 which in all other respects could have been made a hundred years earlier, yet the date was contemporary with the box. Despite this, I believe it is safe to place a pre-1650 date to boxes bearing Classical motifs provided that other features are early.

There is also a "feel" to an early box which is difficult to describe. We tend to forget in comparing two boxes that there may be a hundred years between them; subtle differences in the surfaces are very often not too apparent, but they must exist, and with practice an experienced eye may detect these. Certainly, if it is possible to view a group of boxes together minute changes in surface texture (beneath the patina) do become apparent on close examination; all the early boxes in my collection seem "at home" together.

The difference in surface texture is apparent in the following illustrations; with equal patina nevertheless there is a hundred years of wear absent in the lower box; each panel was tangentially sawn. The "grain" in each panel is presented at an equal angle to the surface; both panels are of oak which was tangentially sawn.

EARLY FEATURES

1. The Timber.

The timber sources analysis (page s 67/68) shows that in my sample up to about the middle of the 17th Century a box could be made from oak which came from one of three sources; from imported (possibly Polish) timber, from oak in managed coppice, or from trees growing in isolation; either from a wood-pasture or wildwood location. It is possible to find timber from all three sources in one box. Very often the carved front panel shows dense annual rings and a fine even grain.

All the early chests are of sawn material; usually to a more or less standard 3/4" thickness. (I have never found a cleft board more than 1/2" thick.) The back boards and the undersides of the bottom boards usually betray a sawn origin from saw tooth marks left in the surface of the wood.

These out of sight places were rarely planed or scraped flat; if they were there is usually still a place or two where the saw cuts are left in the depressions in the surface of the timber. These marks should be reasonably straight and parallel, if circular they are modern and the whole thing should be viewed with distrust. The setting of pit saw teeth must have been quite savage to have left some of the deeper marks.

Cleft oak panels, whether home grown or imported, were usually about 1/4" thick and the cleaving process left longitudinal splits and tears which again are found on those surfaces of the timber which are not visible from the outside, these surfaces were not worked down so thoroughly. Cleft panels will always show medullary rays on both surfaces, and the presence of these on the surface of a box is usually the first indication that it is made from either cleft or quarter-sawn timber.

There is usually a variation in the thickness of the timber in early boxes; this may be only a matter of a millimetre or so, but it can be quite considerable.

Timber was imported in both sawn and cleft states, and I believe that many of the panels (particularly the carved front panels) in the early boxes which show dense ring sequences may be from sessile oak which was brought into the country. Over half of the early boxes have timber with dense ring-widths. Four of the early boxes have ring densities in excess of 30 to the inch, and I doubt whether English trees would produce growth this slow across the widths of the boards which they occupy. The outer parts of very old trees in demise might have produced these ring widths but this timber would not cleave (although it could have been sawn). Old trees in this condition usually produce large quantities of shoots on the surface of the timber, but there is no evidence of these; the material is always knot-free over perhaps 30" of board. One of the boxes which is almost certainly of Border Counties origin (no.19) has oak of this character which would indicate that this was available far inland, but this is not surprising when one remembers that rivers were extensively used for transport of materials at the time, and the Severn served the Border Counties for this purpose.

The effort of making small quantities of boards from local sources was probably not worth while if better imported stock was available, and the imported timber was probably competitive in price as it was mechanically sawn on the Continent, probably by water-power.

Prior to the mid-17th Century, with the home-grown timber in the illustrated boxes, sixteen out of thirty have boards from obviously coppice sources; seventeen have boards from open-grown trees, and three have material from both. In the second part of our period, from about 1650 to 1720, 11 of the 14 boxes contain timber which came from open-grown trees; only three also contain wood from a coppice origin. We know that a shortage of timber had developed by about 1630 and it would appear from the evidence in the boxes that coppice sources diminished soon afterwards. Only one of the later boxes contained cleft timber. The coppice systems produced the smaller diameter trees that had long been favoured as a source of raw material due to the lesser effort needed to fell, extract, and convert the timber. This was particularly so in house building, where considerable quantities of small dimensioned timber were used. A sudden increase in demand may have been impossible to fulfil from these sources which by this time probably only yielded suitably sized timber every twenty to forty years. This would force the use of the bigger old trees outside the coppiced areas, which had previously been avoided.

After about 1650, hardly any coppice timber appears in the boxes.

With regard to the raw material, early boxes should contain cleft timber; this is more likely to have a coppice source, and the panels will have random thicknesses particularly if cleft. Early chests will be of sawn timber only, of more or less even thickness.

2. Mouldings.

We know that there was little or no innovation in the design or development of woodworking tools for a very considerable period; tools, once evolved to suit their purpose, remained the same. There is very little evidence in the early boxes of the use of moulding planes. These must have been difficult to make, and many workshops probably just did not have such a tool, having relied for generations on the simple home-made scratch block. This was easily made by simply filing the profile of the required moulding section into the edge of a flat piece of metal and clamping this between two pieces of wood, with the filed edge protruding sufficiently to enter the wood to the correct depth. Passing this back and forth along the length of timber gradually produced the moulding. The tool was best able to produce sections of a quite shallow half-round shape, which was more easily accomplished along the top edge of a panel, and not on the side. Profiles produced by this tool are shown in Figure 7, (see page 64) at A, B, C, D, F, and G. All these are from the lids of early boxes; A is from the lid of box no. 1. Sections A to G are all pre 1650. Sections I, J, and K are later and produced with a moulding plane. Sections E and H seem to crop at all periods. E produced possibly by scraping; H with a flat chisel.

This lid surface decoration is one of the first things I look at when encountering a new box, but here again one cannot be too dogmatic. Scratch block moulding is an early practice but moulding plane work can be found on early pieces, usually in boxes of better workmanship. On the evidence of the illustrated boxes, however if scratch block moulding is found, it is likely to be of an early date.

Moulding along the bottom edges of the boxes is rarer; some have none at all, the maker having simply rounded off the edges of the protruding bottom boards. Deep bottom mouldings are usually associated with the better made boxes, but not necessarily of an early date. Generally, if they are present in a box it tends to be before 1650. The bottom mouldings on later boxes are more meagre in depth and detail. Similarities in bottom moulding sections could provide a clue to a region, if not a workshop of origin. (See boxes 25 and 32).

3. Carving.

The classical motifs so popular in early boxes lend themselves to deep carving; the front panels usually reflect this in their thickness. The exception is the strapwork design occasionally encountered which is usually carved in low relief, in the architectural fashion. All the early boxes show Renaissance influences; their absence in a box makes one look towards the end of the 17th Century.

4. Construction.

Butting or rebating of the joints between the boards is no indicator of date, as each occurs over the whole period. The dovetailing of a joint is usually a late feature, although again one cannot be sure. The superb Welsh desk, (Box 56) is dovetailed, but dated 1635. For that matter, the Egyptians used the joint. The reason that it is not often found in early work is probably that it was difficult to make.

The size of the nails used to secure the joints in boxes is probably quite a good indicator of date; the earlier boxes all contain nails with thick heads, and the size of these is usually all too evident by the amount of staining of the oak. Because of this, or perhaps because smaller nails became available, the later makers used smaller ones, sometimes punching them below the surface of the wood. Dowels were sometimes employed instead of nails, but are no guide to period; they are usually however a guide to good quality.

On some early chests, the strap hinges were external, being nailed down on top of the lids.

Fig. 7.   Lid surface/edge mouldings; sections not to scale.

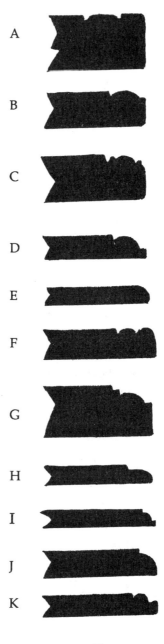

A

B

C

D

E

F

G

H

I

J

K

LATE FEATURES

These can be summarised as follows:

1. Almost all the later boxes are constructed of sawn timber.
2. The annual rings will probably not indicate a coppice source.
3. There is a uniformity in the thickness of the timber used in construction, with a better finish to the inside of the box.
4. Mouldings will be made with a plane instead of a scratch block.
5. The carving is more likely to be shallow, with extensive use of the "V" tool to draw the outlines of the design into the surface.
6. There is unlikely to be punch-mark decoration.
7. There may be dovetailed joints.
8. The joints may show evidence of glue. Nails will have small heads.
9. A deep reddish colour may indicate staining by the maker.
10. There may be internal locks on chests and boxes, where only a keyhope appears on the front panel.

I have made little mention of ironwork in the above; shapes and styles show little variation over the period. Ring hinges are generally held to be early, but I have seen them on a Victorian chest. I had hoped that chemical analysis of the metal in the boxes would be a guide to dating, but as smelting methods did not change substantially over the period I am told that this will not help.

For each of the illustrated boxes in the remaining part of the book I give details of the features which I consider place it in one period or another. Although there is a division in the timber sources analysis at about 1650, stylistically the boxes appear to fall into three categories, with a first period up to about 1620, a middle period to about 1650, and a later up to about 1720. I have done my best to target dates more precisely than the usual "early" "mid" and "late", however, my dates can still only be regarded as suggested periods into which the various boxes appear to fall. I doubt whether we will ever be able to put a precise date to something made three hundred years ago.

Perhaps this is just as well; a great deal of the fascination of these antique items lies in their anonymity

In all the following illustrations I give details of ring widths and sequences. The ring densities vary from 4 to about 12 to the inch, and I suggest that as these are the maximum for each box they should represent the maximum possible rate of growth for the site in which the trees grew. From that it should be possible to roughly match them to the yield classes for oak across the country. In broad terms the thesis appears to have some validity. Timber from the 1987 hurricane has been travelling the country ever since, and some of it has turned up in local timber yards, where I have been making ring-counts of logs from various areas; these, on average, show the variations which I expect to find. Whatever the climate in the 16th and 17th Centuries, our weather has always come from the Atlantic, and proportions of rainfall today cannot be different from one part of the country to another than they were hitherto. Much more work is needed to confirm the hypothesis, and I am well aware that the sample of 44 boxes is a small one in statistical terms.

For the rest of the book I will leave the various chests, desks and boxes to speak for themselves.

Date	Box No	Max H/Grown	Import R.P.I.	Coppice Source	Open Source	All Home	Sewn Cleft	Possible Origin
1550-1600	1	6	-	yes	-	yes	S	West
1580-1620	2	5.7	23	no	yes	no	S	West
pre 1600	3	6	-	yes	-	yes	S	West
1590-1610	4	12	20	yes	-	no	S	East
1590-1610	5	11	-	no	yes	yes	S/C	East
1590-1610	6	11	30	no	yes	yes	S/C	East
1600-1630	7	4	20	no	yes	no	S/C	West
1600-1620	8	9	32	yes	yes	no	S	East
1600-1620	9	12	20	yes	-	no	C	East
1600-1620	10	5.5	-	yes	-	yes	S/C	West
1600-1620	11	6	-	yes	-	yes	S	Hereford
1600-1620	12	8	-	no	yes	yes	S/C	
1600-1620	13	6.8	-	no	yes	yes	S/C	West
1600-1625	14	7	32	yes	no	no	S/C	Devon
1600-1650	15	5	-	no	yes	yes	S	West
1630	16	4	24	no	yes	yes	S	Glos
1620-1650	17	6	24	no	yes	no	S	West
1600-1620	18	10	-	yes	-	yes	S	
1620-1630	19	8	30	yes	-	no	C	
1630-1640	20	6	-	yes	-	yes	S/C	West
1630-1640	21	8	24	yes	-	yes	S	
1630-1650	22	5	-	yes	-	yes	S/C	West
1620-1640	23	5	-	no	yes	yes	C	West
1620-1640	24	7	26	no	yes	no	S	West
1620-1640	25	5	-	yes	-	yes	S/C	Devon
1620-1630	26	10	-	yes	yes	yes	S	
1630-1640	27	8	-	no	yes	yes	S	
1640-1660	28	5	-	no	yes	yes	S/C	Somerset
1630-1640	29	6	-	no	yes	yes	S	Glos

1650-1660	30	6	-	yes	yes	yes	S	Wilts
Date 1674	31	6	20	no	yes	yes	C	West
1660-1680	32	5	-	yes	-	yes	S	Devon
1660-1680	33	7	-	yes	-	yes	S	West
1660-1680	34	4.5	-	no	yes	yes	S	West
1680-1700	35	10	-	yes	-	yes	S	
Date 1694	36	4	-	no	yes	yes	S	West
1680-1700	37	5	-	no	yes	yes	S	West
1700	38	5	-	no	yes	yes	S	West
Date 1711	39	8	-	no	yes	yes	S/C	
1700-1720	40	4	-	no	yes	yes	S	Wales
1700-1720	41	5	-	no	yes	yes	S	Wales
1720-1740	42	10	-	no	yes	yes	S	
Date 1719	43	7.9	-	no	yes	yes	S	West
1700-1720	44	7	-	no	yes	yes	S	West

"Bible" box dimensions, analysis.

		Length	Width	Depth
Box no. 4	1590-1610	31"	20"	9½"
Box no. 5	1580-1620	26"	16"	8½"
Box no. 6	1590-1610	24½"	16"	7½"
Box no. 9	1600-1620	20"	12"	8¾"
Box no. 10	1600-1620	17"	10½"	8"
Box no. 11	1600-1620	26"	21"	10"
Box no. 14	1600-1625	22"	15"	7½"
Box no. 16	1630	28½"	20"	9¾"
Box no 17	1620-1650	28"	20"	9"
Box no. 19	1620-1630	20"	16"	10½"
Box no. 20	1630-1640	26"	16"	8"
Box no. 23	1620-1640	18½"	12½"	8½"
Box no. 24	1620-1640	26½"	15½"	8½"
Box no. 25	1620-1640	25"	16"	8"
Box no. 27	1630-1640	21½"	13½"	6½"
Box no. 28	1640-1660	29"	16"	9"
Box no. 30	1650-1660	27½"	15½"	6½"
Box no. 31	Dated 1674	24"	17"	10"
Box no. 33	1660-1680	30½"	17½"	11½"
Box no. 34	1660-1680	29"	18"	10"
Box no. 35	1680-1700	28"	15½"	10"
Box no. 36	Dated 1694	22"	16"	9"
Box no. 37	1680-1700	27"	18"	10"
Box no. 38	Dated 1711	27"	12"	8"
Box no. 40	1700-1720	31"	17¾"	10"
Box no. 41	1700-1720	23"	13"	8½"
Box no. 42	1720-1740	23"	14"	10"
Box no. 43	Dated 1719	28½"	16"	9"

From this sample, the average depth of boxes pre about 1660 = 8.47"

post about 1660 = 9.64"

The average volume of boxes pre about 1660 = 3318 sq"

post about 1660 = 4076 sq"

Post 1660 this is an increase of 14 percent in the depth of the boxes, and a 23 percent increase in the volume. The "average" box had obviously to cope with more contents; or did some new use arise towards the end of the century?

CHESTS, DESKS

&

BOXES

Box no.1.   Length 40" Width 13¾" Height 22½"

c. 1550-1600

All the oak in this chest was sawn; most of the boards are ¾" thick. Due to coarse saw cuts, assessment of ring widths is difficult; however those visible on the tops of the side panels show rapid growth at a maximum of 6 rings to the inch; the lid has a definite coppice origin with fast growth on each side of ten narrow rings. None of the boards was quarter sawn; there are no visible medullary rays. Knots of up to 1½" diameter are present in some of the boards; the timber probably came from a section of the tree just above the knot-free butt, just below the heavier branches of the crown. The very broad annual rings indicate growth in a high rainfall area; this shows up in the highly eroded surface of the lid. Over the centuries, the softer tissue in the annual rings has worn away, leaving the denser summer wood in ridges along the grain of the wood.

The decoration of the front panel was mainly accomplished with a ½" gouge, in imitation perhaps of pierced woodwork of a much earlier date. There are three distinct shapes; an inverted heart (or perhaps a tree) beneath the lock plate, lozenges, and crude flowers. The running lines on the top and bottom of the front panel are simple scratch block channels, these occur on the lid also. On the lower front panel is a diamond design of incised lines which is also enriched with punch marks of a star shape. The

triangular "apron" pieces look added but they are contemporary.

The sides of the chest are set an inch or so inside the ends of the front and back panels which could be a Westcountry feature; it was probably also a device to prevent the boards splitting when nailed.

The lock plate is original and upside down. I wonder why the maker left it as it is; if locks and hasps came together from the blacksmith (and they surely did) this would have necessitated the making of a longer hasp, and it would certainly have been quicker to remove the lock and put it the right way up.

The original ring hinges are still in the backboard, the ones in the lid are a replacement. All the joints are simply butted and nailed, the nails are substantial. The construction is crude, with no attempt at a "finish". The presence of lozenge decoration on the front panel, with scratch block moulding of the most primitive nature together with the whole "look" of the chest incline me to the suggested date. If the panels were completely pierced through this could be a hundred years earlier; it was perhaps a copy of an earlier piece.

The colour of the oak in this chest is a deep rich red brown, and despite the erosion of the surfaces of some of the panels, where it exists the patina is high.

Length 40" Width 15¾" Height 22"

c. 1580-1620.

Although the visible boards in this chest are of oak, the back and the bottom are of elm. Many chests have this mix of timbers, presumably to reduce the cost; many more must have disappeared due to insect attack in the elm. All the timber in this chest was sawn, the boards average ¾" thick. None of the boards are quarter-sawn. The top and the sides are of home-grown oak, one side was cut from the very centre of a tree and shows the innermost ring and the following 40 years' growth. This was steady at 5.7 rings to the inch indicating that the tree was free-standing for at least this period. The front board has a completely different ring-structure; this was tangentially sawn from a log of at least 14" diameter with an average ring density of 23 to the inch; almost certainly imported timber.

The timber which produced the lid was not completely seasoned when the long external strap hinges were fitted; shrinkage has forced a kink in the left-hand hinge.

The chamfered step below the front panel on each of the sides is an attractive feature and is usually the sign of an early piece (as are the external strap hinges.)

The lid has a simple scratch block moulding around all four edges; this overlaps at the corners, and has the usual early half round section "C" (page 64) formed on top of the board. This is typical of the period as are the generous ascending curves which originally started a few inches from the bottom of the side boards; considerable wear over the years has eroded the parts of these boards in contact with the ground, but the "step" is still present on front of the left-hand board.

All the joints in the chest are butted, and the nails are substantial. There is a precision in the construction of this chest which is absent in the previous example. The metalwork in the chest is also substantial; it would have been difficult to break into. All the nails securing the hinges and the lock protrude into the middle of the chest and were clenched. The tapered portion of the hasp fits into a recessed ornamental plate which is rivetted to the lock-plate. This would make it difficult to obtain any real leverage on the hasp itself if one attempted to force the lock.

The bottom of the chest is narrower than the top, which gives it a more elegant shape than the more usual square section.

Although uncarved, the chest has so many early features that I am fairly confident as to the dating. All the metalwork in the chest is original apart from the right-hand hinge, which is a well made replacement.

The colour of the timber is a deep dark rich brown, with a glass-like patina; it has always been well cared for, unlike so many of the early plain chests.

Detail: ornamental lock-plate and hasp on Box no.2.

Box no.3.   Length 44½" Width 15" Heights 21"

Pre- 1600

Here is the poor relation of the previous chest, the standard safe cum filing cabinet of the slightly better off for perhaps three centuries. It is very substantial; again all the boards are sawn, and are about 1" thick throughout. The back and bottom boards are of elm, all the rest are oak showing considerable erosion.

All the oak was home grown with ring densities varying from 6 to 16 to the inch. The lid has an interesting sequence of three narrow rings followed by ten years of average growth, followed by a further three narrow rings. I cannot find a sequence of droughts and normal years to fit this pattern and conclude that this was in fact a coppice rotation where the coppice regrowth was cut as soon as it began to seriously compete with the oak beneath which it grew; this must have occurred on two occasions and hints at an actively managed area. The ten year interval is interesting; this was quite common at the time when the box may have been made.

Dating these plain chests is always difficult and very often one can only rely on the ironwork; in this chest one clue lies in the sparse lozenge ornament on the lockplate keyhole cover, the lock is the one originally fitted to the chest. On the backboard there remains an impression of the original flat fishtail hinge, beside a 17th Century replacement.

On the lid of the chest there is a simple channel moulding running on the top surface along the front edge; this has the same section as the lid moulding on box no. 1.

The chest is not particularly well made, indeed although one side of the lid has been cut square, the other has not; this is not recent damage.

Box no.4.   Length 31" Width 20" Depth 9½"

c. 1590-1610.

This impressive box is constructed throughout of sawn oak. Most of the panels are substantial 1/2" thick; the bottom boards are just over 1/4". Apart from some of the bottom boards none of the timber has been sawn on the quarter; the average ring count is about 12 to the inch, indicating an eastern origin for the timber. Some of the bottom boards, which run back-to-front instead of laterally, have very dense annual rings in excess of 20 to the inch. The widest board is of coppice origin. The even texture of the timber in this box makes me suspect it to be of Sessile oak.

If the box is eastern it could be from Norfolk; although stopped fluting (this particular form of nulling) is fairly universal it was used in that county towards the end of the 16th Century; a dated example exists. The presence of imported timber in the bottom boards would not be surprising; Baltic timber came in through the east coast ports.

Wherever it was made, the first owner was obviously a person of some substance; the construction and carving of the box are of the highest order. There are no nails in the joints, these are made by dowels, and are rebated.

The deep precise carving and the thick bottom moulding give the box an architectural appearance fully in keeping with the better work of the late 16th Century; all the features are classical derivatives. It even looks like a temple.

The lock plate, which is an 18th Century replacement, partially

80

obscures the initials "E.R."; these appear to be contemporary. They contain the remnants of a black wax which at some time was melted into the design to emphasise the lettering, in the same way that wax was melted into the engraved Roman numerals on chapter rings of clock dials. If they were added at some late date, it was before the new lock plate was fitted. I would like to believe that the initials stood for "Elizabeth Regina"; perhaps they do.

This box was in recent use as a container for a video recorder or some such device; the front hinges downwards and there is a hole in the backboard. Fortunately this was done without too much damage to the box; someone had managed to saw through the dowels in the rebated joint; I cannot understand how.

The box has that deep rich honey colour which good oak occasionally attains, and a high patina.

Box no.5.   Length 26" Width 16" Depth 8½"

c. 1580-1620

All the boards in this early box were sawn, apart from the bottom boards which were cleft. The sawn boards are 5/8" thick, the cleft are 1/4". None of the oak was quarter-sawn; thus there are no medullary rays visible in the timber. This is surprising; normally at least the top exhibits some rays for visual effect. Here the top is made from two boards the widest of which is 13"; this was tangentially sawn. The direction of the grain in the remaining panels is haphazard; I suspect that these were all cut from one log which perhaps was a second length, from a point in the trunk of the tree where branches occurred.

There is no evidence in the annual rings of a coppice origin for the timber, the relatively even rate of growth of about 11 rings to the inch indicates a free-standing tree from perhaps a wood-pasture location. With such even growth, the maximum rate of growth is about the average rate of growth. There is one ring on the front panel of 1/8" but as it is the only ring of this size in the whole box, for purposes of comparison I am ignoring this.

The carving on the front panel is carried round to the sides, and I wonder whether the provision of four and a half roses only on the front panel was accidental. One is tempted to think that here is further evidence that carving was carried out over quite long pieces of oak which were cross-cut to the required length; however the semi-rose of the front panel is partnered by another matching one on the side panel, making the

design run coherently around the box. Also, of course, with a running design such as this guilloche banding there would be no provision for margins, left and right, at the required lengths, here a margin has been provided on the right hand side of the panel. An occasional lack of balance in design does not appear to have bothered Tudor customers unduly; this occurs in other boxes and items of furniture.

The design of the roses within the guilloche bands is different; there are two varieties which presumably represent the emblems of the houses of York and Lancaster; taken in conjunction with the use of the Renaissance banding this helps to date the box. Guilloche is another import from the Mediterranean, with a Near Eastern origin that came into Continental Europe through Rome. It was a great favourite in Elizabethan times. The deep confident carving of this motif is typical of the late 16th Century.

The joints in this box are all nailed and rebated; the hinges are a 17th Century replacement. The internal lock is unusual on early boxes; the one on this box is not the original, but is probably 18th Century as is the brass escutcheon plate. It is possible that the original box had no lock at all, one being added later.

The box is a deep rich brown in colour, with a high patina.

Only the top of this box is of cleft oak, all the other panels are sawn. It is of quite substantial construction, the front is 1/2" thick and the two sides are nearly 1". The back panel was quarter-sawn, but the front was cut tangentially; both of these panels have very dense ring-widths across their whole width (see page 29) and are almost certainly from imported timber. The lid and the bottom of this box are of home-grown origin; one bottom board shows the typical slowing of growth when the tree meets gradual competition, perhaps from a neighbouring tree in a wildwood situation, or even from the gradual growth of uncut coppice. The maximum rate of growth is 11 rings per inch across the widest board.

The choice of tangentially cut timber for the front panel is odd, and has resulted in the splitting-off of segments of wood from the highest parts of the carving; perhaps the density of the timber attracted the carver. This weakness has been caused by the medullary rays running at right angles to the surface of the board, and not parallel to it. Considerable excavation was necessary to create the design in the front panel. The petals of the flowers are quite deeply undercut, giving a three-dimensional effect to them. The matting in the field of the design disguises the deep marks of the gouge which took out the surplus wood. The work was accomplished with no more than three tools; a "V" tool to outline the design, and two gouges to complete the decoration.

The simple motif has a distinctly "Arabesque" pedigree, deriving from the Eastern Mediterranean plant-stem patterns. The Victoria and Albert

Museum has a damascened bowl of Saracen origin part of the detail of which exactly matches the decoration of this box. The design crops up on embroidery patterns of the late 16th/early 17th Century; the Victoria and Albert museum also has a 16th Century embroidered hood with the same motif.

By the late 16th Century, the desert origin of the flowers would have been forgotten, by then they would have been recognised as Tudor roses and a stylised version of these appears in abundance on beds, coffers and court cupboards right up to about the middle of the 17th Century. The rose was also the symbol of Venus and to a population steeped in superstition an emblem combining the patriotic with the romantic would have had a powerful appeal. The association with Venus would also indicate that this was a lady's box, perhaps a betrothal present.

The lid is undecorated and there is no attempt at moulding, the edges are simply rounded down, as are those of the protruding bottom boards. The deeply rebated joints are all nailed together. The hinges and lock are original. The box is a rich chocolate colour, with a high patina.

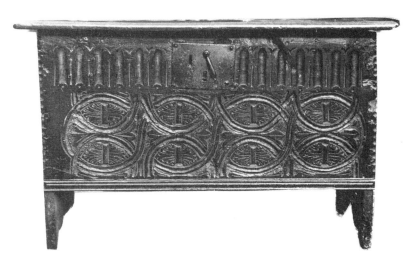

All the panels in this little chest are of sawn oak, apart from the lid, which was cleft. The lid is 5/8" thick, and the other boards are 3/4". The lid has medullary rays, and also displays a ripple on the surface which is always a sign of a cleft board in oak. Ripple occurs in several native hardwoods; opinions vary as to the cause, but the flexing of the bole of the trees in the wind is the most likely. It is unusual in oak; in sycamore it produces the figure-mark known as "fiddle-back" and is highly prized. Where it does occur in oak cleaving emphasises the undulations, which can be quite pronounced, although normally only visible when the board is viewed at an angle.

The end-grain of the lid of the chest shows evidence of extremely fast growth, at a maximum of between three and four annual rings per inch. The front and sides show a quite different rate of growth, at approximately twenty rings to the inch, and came from a different tree, if not from a different country; these boards could well have been imported. Assuming the lid timber to have been produced locally, the tree from which it came must have been standing in a very fertile site in a warm location in an area of high rainfall; being 13½" in width, with the fast rate of growth right across the board, it can hardly have come from a coppice shoot which

would only show a fast rate of growth in the early years. None of the timber in the chest shows signs of a coppice origin.

The decoration of the front panel is typical of the early years of the 17th Century, with a strong Renaissance element in the guilloche ribbon which encircles the inner motifs. The fluting (or nulling) along the top of the panel is no guide to date as it occurs over perhaps a fifty year period, but the lid is moulded on the front and back top surfaces with the familiar early shallow half-round section accomplished with a scratch-block. The carving is deep and confident but of poor workmanship; the laying-out of the design betrays poor draughtsmanship in that the guilloche bands are slightly to the left of the upper fluting. Such inaccuracies seem to have had little importance at the time; they occur on many items.

The chest has two features which are strongly Westcountry. The chipped decoration on each side of the front panel, which also occurs on the sides of the lid, appears on many Westcountry chests and boxes, and the applied moulding strip along the bottom of the panel is a feature of many chests from the area.

The lock-plate appears to be the original, but the chest has had two sets of hinges before the present ones.

The colour is a rich deep brown, with a high patina.

Box no.8   Length 35½" Width 13" Height 22"

c. 1600-1620

All the oak in this chest was sawn; the original thickness must have been 3/4", shrinkage and planing have reduced this to 5/8". All the boards were cut tangentially and thus there are no visible medullary rays. The back and front boards exhibit very slow growth at an average of 32 rings to the inch; the timber in the lid had a quite different origin, showing a gradual growth over 40 years of from 9 to 20-plus rings to the inch, with an average of 10.6. This growth pattern is consistent with a tree growing in a wildwood situation, perhaps as part of a group. The top of one of the side panels exhibits a fifteen year period of faster growth between two sequences of narrower rings; this timber could well have been produced by a coppice system.

The timber in the chest contains knots of varying diameters up to 1½"; the lid, made from one board now 13" wide has split and a modern repair made by glueing. This split was more likely to have been caused by use than shrinkage, although there would have been some tension set up between the innermost nails securing the hinges and the strap of the hasp.

The ornamental profile of the side panels is attractive and typical of many small chests of the period. The front and back boards are parallel which gives the chest a less elegant appearance than that of box no. 2.

The moulding around all four edges of the lid and the front panel was made with a scratch- block producing a very shallow half-round profile within incised lines, at the corners these run across each other.

All the joints between the back, front, and side boards are rebated and nailed together. When I bought this chest it was in seven pieces, with only the back board and the rear portion of the lid held together by the hinges. Fortunately, the split in the lid was reasonably straight and by squaring the edges I was able to reconstruct the board. This sort of repair can be detected where there is notched decoration on the edges of the panels, the notches are no longer equidistant at the point of repair unless by chance the removed timber equals the "pitch" of the notches.

I renailed the panels using nails salvaged from a 17th Century beam, through the existing holes. Vinegar and very fine steel wool removed the grey surface grime which had accumulated over the years; vigorous polishing with beeswax brought up a deep warm honey colour and quite a reasonable patina.

One feature of this chest which helps to put it between the suggested dates is the placement of the hinges; the straps are above the lid and not inside the chest, which is more usual in later pieces. Outside hinges are usually (but not invariably) an early feature.

All the metalwork on the chest is original.

Such small chests must have been produced in considerable numbers during the 17th Century for so many of them to remain with us today.

c. 1600-1620

All the panels in this box were cleft and in consequence show very prominent medullary rays. The front and the sides are 1/2" thick, the lid, back, and bottom boards are all 3/8". The front board shows a very clear coppice sequence, with 16 years of fast growth followed by 12 years of restricted growth followed by 10 years of fast, ending in a long period of slow growth to the end of the panel. This is consistent with intensively managed coppice-with-standards, where the standard trees were left at rather less than a final crop spacing. After the removal of the final coppice understorey, the oaks were left to form a tight canopy and grow on for a period in excess of 70 years.

There is proof in this box that oak with densely packed annual rings could be cleft; several of the boards show ring densities in excess of 20 to the inch. The timber came from a completely knot-free log, and again I suspect an imported source. The lid is one board 12" in width, making the diameter of the parent tree at least 24". The lid took the tree 146 years to make, giving a mean ring width density of 12.1 to the inch.

The deep nulling on the front panel gives this small box a decidedly "Norman" look; church windows of about 1050-1200 have rounded tops in the same proportion. However, as a decorative form the shape has a much earlier ancestry, it appears as a marginal decoration on a Corinthian

black-figure vase of the 5th Century BC (page 54). At the end of the 16th Century it perhaps had an architectural origin; it appears in pattern books of the period.

This form of carving is easily accomplished and must have been a quick way of decorating surfaces; it appears on friezes and table rails right through the Jacobean period, dying out at about the Restoration except on "Country" furniture.

The carving on this box is bold and deep; hence the choice of 1/2" timber for the front panel. At one time the box had a lock; this was replaced with the inset carved piece of timber more easily seen in the large illustration. This was particularly well done; the craftsman even took the trouble to match the grain of the rest of the panel.

The lid has a simple scratch block moulding (see section B, page 64) on the upper surfaces of the front and back edges. Each side of the lid has been embellished with a series of fairly broad notches. The lid displays very pronounced medullary rays which protrude perhaps 2mm above the surface; this "figure" marking would have been very distinctive when new, and no doubt the timber was chosen for this reason.

All the joints in the box are simply butted and nailed; the hinges are the second set, with flat "fishtail" ends.

The box has a deep blackish-brown colour, with a high patina. The initials "E.F." are incised into the bottom of the front panel. (I did not notice these until I produced the enlarged photograph.)

Box no.10.   Length 17" Width 10½" Depth 8"

c. 1600-1620

The lid of this little box is made from cleft oak; all the other boards are sawn. The thickness of the sawn panels varies at about 1/2", the lid is 1/4". (This seems to be a fairly standard thickness for early cleft oak panels.) The bottom board is 1/4" thick and was nailed to the bottom of the box before it was fully seasoned; it has a quite serious split some 9" long. This bottom board came from a young tree which was growing rapidly at 5½ to 6 rings to the inch; a similar rate of growth is displayed in the front and back panels, and the lid.

The bottom board was cut tangentially from near the centre of the tree, and it is possible by projecting the curvature of the rings to estimate the minimum diameter of the log which produced the board; this was about 12". Fast growth in a tree of this diameter almost certainly indicates a coppice-with-standards origin, with the tree being felled some 35 years after springing from a stool. The area in which it stood could have produced two fifteen year old crops during this period. If the coppice was being actively managed, cutting the underwood species before it formed a canopy with the young oak could have prevented a slowing-down in the growth of the latter; this box has no signs of periodic restricted growth; nevertheless I think the evidence of fast growth is strong enough to give

97

the timber a coppice origin.

The lid has shallow scratch-block moulding around all four edges, with a flattened half-round section, it also has incised marginal decoration repeating the chevron pattern on the front panel.

The carving is a strapwork derivative based on the "S" curve. The carving in low relief on the front panel of this box has a strong architectural flavour; there are Classical undertones in the honeysuckle-like elements in the "S" scroll, which had a Greek origin. There is very similar decoration on the front panel of box no. 12.

The carving was achieved by the use of only two tools, a deep "V" tool and a gouge to take the surface down to the ground, which is profusely matted. The front panel has extensive decoration in the margins of the design; the angled lines of the chevron strips were made with a straight-edged chisel driven vertically into the wood when this was on the bench. These bands were further embellished by the use of an oblong punch, made simply from a bar of soft iron. These punch marks are also in the margins of the lid. Lombardic initials "A.E." are carved into the centre of the lid.

The hinges, which are the second set, are a hybrid between "butterfly" and round fishtail; the original hinges were of the "ring" type (see page 221). The lock-plate is a modern addition, and lacks a slot for the hasp, which is missing. The box is a deep golden brown in colour, with a high patina.

Box no.11.   Length 26" Width 21" Depth 10"

c.1600-1620

This box has been solidly constructed of sawn oak, most of the boards are 3/4" thick, but the front panel is 1". With deep carving occupying most of the surface of the panels (the sides are also carved) these was no need to display medullary rays and none of the boards was quarter sawn. On the lid there is evidence of a coppice origin, with a twenty year period of fast growth between two periods of slower. The back panel came from a young tree which was initially growing rapidly, and exhibits a maximum rate of growth of 6-7 rings to the inch; after a 25 year period growth slows in this board which again is consistent with a coppice origin. The front board was cut tangentially from a different piece of timber, this averages about 18 rings to the inch, indicating that it may have been cut from the outer circumference of an older tree that was losing its vigour, or again it might be imported. (See page 25. The "Crump" oak produced 16 rings per inch, but only over the last few inches of diameter.)

The broad "S" shaped scroll was very popular during the period; it is a Renaissance architectural feature that strayed onto furniture; it is also found on friezes above panelling. The Royal Commission on Historical Monuments Report on Herefordshire illustrates two panelled rooms with almost identical friezes, both given as mid-17th Century; however, the Old House Museum in Hereford has bargeboards with an elongated version of the same design, from 1621. This box contains an extra element in the

design which I believe may make it earlier; this is the introduction of the small Tudor roses into the scrollwork. These are carved in the same way as those in box no.6 which is late 16th/early 17th Century.

The lid moulding includes the shallow half-round scratchblock section of the early boxes, the lower lip moulding on the lid is a flattish quadrant produced by a chisel; the marks of this tool are still evident. On the top surface of the lid is a marginal decoration made of incised lines about 1/2" apart, with punch marks between them; the same punch was used to decorate the central part of the scrolled curves on the other panels.

This box came to me via the Summerfield sale in Cheltenham; prior to that it had languished in a cellar for thirty years. The bottom moulding strip is missing, as is a strip which ran along the front of the lid.

The hinges are original, of the "ring" type; although the lock appears to be original I believe that it may not be; there is evidence of an earlier hasp on the lower surface of the lid.

Despite its spell in the cellar, the patina, after a few polishes, is high; the colour is a very dark brown.

I believe that there are so many links to Herefordshire in this box that they cannot be merely coincidental. The active management of coppice woodlands in the county has continued from the 16th Century almost to the present day.

Box no.12.   Length 24¾" Width 18" Height 11½"

c.1600-1620.

All the oak in this desk is home grown. The lid, the bottom boards, and the back are all cleft, of 3/8" thickness; all these boards show medullary rays. The front panel and the sides are sawn, of 3/4" thickness. This extra thickness gives stability to the desk and provides adequate timber for the carving, which is 1/4" deep in places.

The average rate of growth of the oak in the desk is about 10 rings to the inch in the back board. The fastest is about 8 rings to the inch, again in the back board; this displays a gradual slowing of growth across 11" from this density to an exceedingly dense 30 rings to the inch in the last few inches, consistent with a board produced towards the outer perimeter of an open-grown tree beginning to lose its vigour.

The front panel and the sides are not quarter-sawn, but the timber is knot-free and straight-grained, as are all the visible boards.

There is no evidence of coppice growth anywhere in the desk.

The desk is very soundly constructed, with shallowly rebated joints which are all nailed together.

The carving is bold and deep as on so many early pieces, the front panel has the familiar plant-stem "S" curves, here terminating in a honeysuckle pattern within the scrolls. This Arabesque-Greek decoration contrasts strongly with the Renaissance motifs on the side panels and gives a Classical appearance to the desk. The design is further enhanced by the inlaid strips of alternating holly and bog-oak which act as margins to the main areas of carving; this is an attractive feature not often found on desks and table-boxes although it is often found on larger pieces of furniture These inlays are carried around to the side panels.

The lock, the hasp and the hinges are all original and are the standard 17th Century fitments. The colour of the desk is a rich deep brown, with a high patina.

Dating this desk from the lid moulding has given me a problem; it has ovolo moulding that has been executed with a moulding plane around all the edges of the lid and the top board; normally one would give this a much later date. The lower moulding is similarly from a plane, but this is a (possibly 18th Century) replacement. However, taking the lid moulding in conjunction with the obviously high quality of the construction of the desk, and the carving, together with the presence of the inlaid margins, I think it safe to give it an early date. The lid of course, could have been replaced later, but there are no signs of this. The whole thing could be a late 17th Century copy of an earlier piece, but it does have the "feel" of an early desk.

All the oak in this desk is home grown, of varying thicknesses. One side is 3/4", the other 1/2"; these are the only sawn boards in the desk. The front panel is 5/8", to accept the deep carving, the lid and bottom boards are 3/8" and 1/4" respectively. Two of the boards are 15" wide in one piece, both are cleft (the lid and the back.) All the cleft panels show rapid growth varying from 6 rings to the inch to 10. The average across the widest panel is 6.8. This rate of growth is reasonably even across the whole width of the panel with only minor variations in ring width due to climatic factors; there is no evidence of a coppice origin, and the timber can only have come from a free-standing tree. This tree must have grown in a locality very similar to Herefordshire; oaks in that county being felled today show ring widths of about this density. Medullary rays are present in all the panels of the desk, including the sawn side panels, and I am reasonably certain that all the timber came from the same tree.

The deeply carved nulling gives this desk a strongly architectural appearance; with the sloping lid, from the front it even looks like a building. It has lost all its bottom moulding, which is a pity, as the presence of moulding similar to that on box no. 4 (which it would probably have had) would have given it an even stronger architectural appearance.

Again, a strong classical look helps to date the desk. in common with the other early boxes it has the same shallow half-round scratch block moulding; this follows all the edges on top of the desk.

The strip of wood planted on the lower edge of the lid to prevent a book from sliding off is not original; I suggest that this is an 18th Century addition, put there at the same time as a new lock was fitted, although with its brass escutcheon plate this latter could even be Victorian. The original lock was much lower down; a timber insert is evident below the lock plate which has been crudely carved in imitation of the earlier nulling. There is a further small repair at the very top of the front panel on the right hand side, which I do not understand. Very often these unexplained repairs are the sign of a cut down piece, but this is not so with this desk.

All the joints are rebated and nailed; the substantial hinges are a hybrid between butterfly and fish tail.

The desk is a rich golden brown with a very high patina. A most attractive feature is the way in which the nulling is carried around to each side, increasing in height to follow the shape of the desk. Within the channels of the nulling are little balloon shaped designs made simply by driving the tips of gouges (of three diameters) vertically into the lower parts of the nulling when the board was flat on the bench.

Box no.14 Length 22" Width 15" Depth 7½"

c.1600-1625

There is an odd mix of timber in this little box. The front, the back, and the bottom boards are all sawn, but one of the sides is cleft. The sawn boards are only 1/4" thick, illustrating how accurately a pit saw could be made to cut. (One sure way of determining whether a board is cleft or sawn is to look for knots. Cleft boards are always knot free for the obvious reason that knots would prevent accurate cleaving.) The side panels are 3/4" thick, no doubt to give rigidity to a box where all the other components are so thin.

The front panel exhibits very dense growth, at about 32 rings to the inch, (see page 29) and was sawn just off the quarter; a few medullary rays appear along the bottom margin of the panel. The other boards were sawn at random. The bottom board, which is 15" wide, gives a maximum growth rate of about 7 rings to the inch; it also shows a coppice sequence of 25 years of slow growth, 20 years of fast, followed by a further period of slow growth. The 25 years of slow growth is a long period for a coppice rotation at this time, and indicates perhaps that the site was neglected, or even forgotten, as some outlying areas are today on large Estates. It is tempting to speculate that this might have been Monastic timber abandoned after the Dissolution.

In this bottom board there are also a series of three dry-summer rings. If my dating of the box is correct these could have been the summers of 1590, 1591, and 1592; they are 23 years back from the end of the board. This would make the timber in the box not younger than about 1615.

With a front panel only 1/4" thick, it was ambitious of the carver to attempt such deep carving; the deeper parts are in fact paper-thin, and in one place penetrate the timber completely; this point has been cunningly disguised as a punch mark.

The double-decker design is an early feature, with the upper storey bearing the traditional leaf motif which occurs frequently on West Country furniture.There is a similar outline in the design of the front panel in box no. 25.

The lower deck carries a row of thistles which were a Stuart emblem.

Unfortunately the lid is a modern replacement; at this date I would have expected the original to have scratch block moulding, or to have been simply rounded-off as in box no. 6. There are no signs that the box ever had a lower moulding.

The lock plate appears original, it even has a key. The original hinges were flat fishtails, remnants of one are still attached to the back board.

The box has a deep golden colour, with a good patina.

This robust commodious travelling chest is constructed entirely of sawn oak, all of 3/4" thickness except the top, which is 1¼". The lid was sawn tangentially with about 5 rings to the inch across the fastest growing section. The back board shows a possible coppice origin, with a reduction in growth from 5 rings to the inch to 10, followed by further rapid growth. The average rate of growth is 35 rings over 6", which is 5.8 to the inch. The presence of single boards some 17" in width in the chest indicates a parent tree of at least 3 feet in diameter; such a tree would have been standing well above any coppice regrowth for a very considerable period. I am more inclined to believe however that the timber came from a wildwood tree standing near others. The slowing in growth could have been caused by competition from a neighbour, the subsequent increase following its removal by man or gale.

The similar rate of growth in the lid indicates a local source common to all the timber in the chest, but the lid with its ironwork originally came from a much earlier piece. One clue to this lies in the timber, the lid is very deeply eroded. Another lies in the moulding on the lid; around three sides this is a fairly standard scratch block moulding, on the fourth this is missing, and the edge has been crudely chamfered. The original lid was perhaps twice as long and may have carried two sets of "Y" shaped iron straps. The eye bolt over which the hasp fits has been driven straight into a conventional 17th Century lock. The present hinges are "H" shaped, but on the lid at one side is evidence of an earlier 8" strap hinge; this does not coincide with any corresponding marks of the back board.

The two substantial carrying handles have similar decoration to the top strap and probably came from the chest which originally claimed the lid.

The chest has no particular claim to fame and I include it partly for the information locked up in the timber and partly as an example of how much of the past history of a piece can be gleaned from small details. Evidence of hinges past and present is always worthy of close examination; at first glance this chest looked "all of a piece" until I opened the lid.

All the joints are rebated for extra strength; the nails which hold the whole thing together are the largest I have ever seen in a chest; the heads exceed 1/2" in diameter.

The chest was obviously made to stand up to considerable wear and tear. The lid is the colour of pale honey, which is probably due to bleaching in sunlight; the rest of the boards have a dull brown colour with no patina worth mentioning. Although it has notched decoration on each side of the front panel, it was not made for display; hence the lack of polish.

Another imposing box, made more so by the depth of the bottom moulding. All the oak in this box is sawn; the top and front panels were quarter sawn to emphasise the figure of the medullary rays. The top is 5/8" thick, all the other boards are 3/4" or thereabouts making it of very substantial construction. Together with the fine quality of the carving, which extends also to the side panels, this would have originally been an expensive purchase.

The timber is all home grown and knot free. The ring density in the front panel slows from a very fast 4 rings to the inch to a fairly sudden 12. The average across the board is 5.2 rings to the inch. The back board on the other hand, exhibits very slow growth throughout, at 24 rings to the inch; this board is sawn tangentially and this rate of growth may not be typical as the ring density can only be counted across the thickness of the board. there is no sign of a coppice rotation anywhere in the box; the lid had been made from two boards, the widest of which shows growth across 13" from 12 rings to the inch to 22, decelerating; this timber must have come from a tree experiencing competition over a long period, and is quite untypical of that which made the other panels in the box. With the fastest growth rate at 1/4" per annum the tree which produced the front panel must have grown in a higher rainfall area, on a particularly fertile site.

I have been told that the opposing lunette decoration below the lock

plate was a Gloucestershire feature; if this is correct it would indicate a Severn Valley origin for the timber, which would be consistent with the rate of growth. (The box is lined with a copy of the *Wilts and Gloucestershire Standard* for June 2nd 1888; there is just a chance that this is a box which remained in the locality of its origin; it was in Tetbury in 1990.)

This refined strapwork was popular during the later years of Elizabeth, but seems to have reached its period of most extensive use in the early/mid 17th Century. It is the ancient "S" curve in another form, with foliar extensions reminiscent of acanthus decorations, and on this box it is carved in very low relief, in the architectural fashion. The background is enhanced by matting with a small punch.

All the joints in the box are rebated. Surprising the joints are nailed; in a box of this quality it would have been more usual to find them dowelled. The patina on the lid and front panel is good; on the side panels, which are carved to the same high quality as the front, the edges of the carving are still sharp to the touch, no doubt because these panels received much less polishing. The colour of the timber is that of milk chocolate. The ring hinges are original, the hasp and lock are later replacements. The extreme width of the box leads me to wonder whether it was designed for a particular purpose. Or did richer purchasers have more to lock away?

Box no.17.   Length 28" Width 20" Depth 9"

1620-1650

For the suggested period this is a very large box; with most of the timber about 3/4" thick it is also very heavy. Only the two boards which make up the lid are quarter-sawn, all the rest have been cut "through and through" at random. On the lower surfaces of the lid some pit-saw marks are still apparent, showing a rate of advancement through the log of about 1/4" per stroke; i.e. the planks were cut from a log of fairly small diameter. The widest board in the lid is 10½" across, with no traces of sapwood.The minimum diameter of the log from which this piece of timber could have been cut from the heartwood would therefore be about 16". Both of the lid boards are from very slow grown timber, at about 24 rings to the inch, and this is surprising as with small-diameter timber one could expect this to have been coppice-grown with a fast rate of growth. The two bottom boards of the box both show a fast growth at about a maximum of 6 to 7 rings to the inch; these are obviously home-grown.

It is possible of course that the two top boards were cut from a much older and larger tree which had already been cut into smaller baulks; this would explain the fast rate of progress of the saw through the timber. On the other hand, the steady slow rate of growth in the lid boards is consistent with that of imported timber perhaps selected by the maker for the medullary rays on the top surfaces. There is an evenness of distance between the saw marks which could be the result of mechanical sawing; and we know that the Poles had developed water-powered sawmills by the seventeenth century.

The box shares many constructional features with the Hereford box (No.11), although it is a little larger. The moulding on the top surface of the lid is virtually identical, moreover although the timber in this box shows no evidence of a coppice rotation, some of it has the same rate of growth as in the earlier box.

The carving of the Lunettes is particularly well executed, and this motif is carried round onto the side panels, always an attractive feature. The punched decoration within the Lunette bands indicates an earlier rather than a later date.

The original hinges were of the flat fish-tail variety, surprisingly replaced by ring hinges, which are usually earlier. The lock, too, is a replacement. There are just a few scraps of black and white block-printed wallpaper still glued inside the box.

Originally the box had moulding around the base.

The colour of the box is a deep rich brown, with a good patina.

Box no.18.   Length 51" Width 18½" Height 23"

c. 1600-1620

Another robust chest, showing signs of considerable "improvement". Solidly constructed of 3/4" sawn oak boards, all of home grown origin. The back board shows very clearly what appear to have been at least two coppice rotations, with ten year periods between intervals of slower growth. The fastest rate of growth within these sequences is about 10 rings to the inch. None of the timber has been quarter sawn; this would have been superfluous anyway on the front panel with so much of the surface excavated in the production of the design.

The two periods of slower growth on the back board are interesting. This board is 14" in width, giving a minimum diameter for the tree from which it came of at least two feet six inches (allowing for sapwood.) If this is not a tree from a coppice-with-standards system, this could be early evidence of deliberate thinning among trees with a closed canopy; the sequences look very like those produced under a well managed "high-forest" system today. Under coppice-with-standards when the oak had developed after many cuttings of the underwood their crowns would have been well above the height which the regeneration could reach, and the spreading crowns would gradually reduce the area available for the economic harvesting of the coppice. If the oak standards had originally been left too close together, at some stage the crowns would join and create

120

"high forest" which could have been thinned perhaps twice before clear felling. such events would have produced a similar configuration as that in the back board.

The "apron" on this chest, with its vine-leaf decoration is an addition; the strip of beading running above it along the bottom of the main front panel shows clear signs of coloured varnish which has partially rubbed away on the edges where a polishing cloth would reach. I believe everything beneath the front panel to be a Victorian Gothic period embellishment. This must have replaced an earlier lower board of some shape, as the bottom board of the chest is some 1½" lower than the bottom edge of the front panel, removal of the vine-leaf board would reveal this gap.

The lid of the chest has the early scratch block shallow half round moulding within a stepped lip, which runs around three sides.

The strapwork carving is in fairly high relief and is made more prominent due to the blacking of the whole of the background. This I believe is original as it does not occur in the vine-leaf decoration beneath. The flowing curves of the strapwork are typical of the better work of the period; beneath the lock plate is a blank shield which must have been intended for a Coat of Arms, one wonders why it was never completed.

The joints are simply butted and nailed, not rebated.

The colour of the oak is a rich red brown, the patina is good.

Box no.19.   Length 20" Width 16" Depth 10½"

c. 1620-1630

All the oak in this box has been cleft. The top and the bottom are 1/4" thick, the sides and the front are 1/2", presumably to accept the deep carving. There are two distinct timber sources; the front panel and the two bottom boards average about 30 rings to the inch, whereas all the other timber in the box is of home grown origin, averaging 8.86 to the inch across the widest board. Due to centuries of ingrained polish, it is difficult to determine ring sequences in some of the panels, but one shows a series of narrower rings which probably gives it a coppice provenance. The widest board shows reasonably even growth, where the maximum ring width is about the average.

As one would expect with cleft timber, medullary rays are prominent on all the plain surfaces of the panels, including the bottom boards. They are somewhat obscured by the carving on the front and the sides.

Interlacing lunettes occur frequently in the English/Welsh border counties; indeed identically carved panelling in an overmantel at Upper Nash Farm, near Presteigne, is illustrated in the Royal Commission on Historical Monuments report on Herefordshire, this is attributed to the early 17th Century. If this box is of Border county origin, the average ring density of nearly nine to the inch seems to bear this out; the counties lying in the shadow of the Welsh mountains produce somewhat narrower annual rings than other counties with a higher rainfall. The presence of boards with 30 rings to the inch is interesting; if this is imported timber it had travelled a long way from port. On the other hand the river Severn was navigable at the time over a considerable distance.

The classical lunettes with acanthus leaf infilling lead me to place the box in the early part of the century. The combination of the two motifs give the box a strong Mediterranean atmosphere; it must have appeared particularly exotic at the time.

The lid has margins decorated with a zig-zag pattern made with a punch about 1" wide. At one time it hinged from the back in the normal way, but the original lid split about 5" from the back, and instead of carrying out the normal repair with battens, the split was squared off, and the narrower strip nailed to the top of the box. Butterfly hinges were then used to join the wider board to this, probably in the late 17th Century. Squaring the split boards resulted in some loss of width; there is no overhang at the front of the box.

The deep carving appears to have been accomplished with only three tools; a "V" tool, and a large and a small gouge. Here again the carver has chosen timber with a fine even grain for the front panel.

At 10½" the box is much deeper than others of the same period, one wonders why.

The colour is a deep rich golden brown, with a very high patina.

125

Box no.20.   Length 26" Width 16" Depth 8"

c. 1630-1640.

Only the oak in the lid of this box is cleft, all the other panels were sawn. The lid is 1/4" thick, the back and the base boards are 3/8" and the sides and the front are 1/2". None of the sawn boards have been cut "on the quarter". There is evidence of a coppice origin in the timber; in the lid the widest board (at 10½") shows a 20 year period of fast growth between two two periods of slower growth. The narrower boards do not show evidence of a coppice source, but do show rapid growth at a maximum of 6 rings to the inch, which could be typical of young timber in a coppice environment between periods of slower increment. The carved front panel has an average ring density of 9.1 rings to the inch. This latter density is in reasonable accord with the rate of growth of box no. 19 (at 8.86) and that in box no. 33 (at 9.2); all three boxes have interlaced lunettes.

The choice of finer grained timber for the front panel is common to many boxes, but here part of the design split away during the carving process (within the extreme left hand and right hand arches) This initially seems to have occurred in the right hand arch, and the carver then split away an equivalent portion of the left hand arch to match; in an attempt to rectify matters he then used punch marks within the damaged areas; using the same punch that was employed on the rest of the design. Otherwise the carving, though simple, is neat and was accomplished with only a "V" tool and a small gouge. The side panels of the box carry the same

127

decoration as the front.

Internally the box has a neat stay which hinges up from the side panel to prop up the lid when open; the tip of this fits into a small recess in the back panel when folded down.

The edges of the lid are not moulded, they have simply been rounded off (to section E, page 64).

All the metalwork is original, the initials "E.A." have at some time been punched upside-down on the hasp. The hinges are of the round fishtail type.

The colour is very similar to the earlier box no. 19; the patina is high, particularly on the lid.

Box no.21.　　　　Length 28½" Width 17" Height 12½"

c. 1630-1640

All the timber in this desk was sawn; pit-saw marks remain on the back and bottom boards. The lid, the back, and the bottom boards are all 3/8" thick; the sides and the front panel vary a little each side of 3/4".One bottom board shows evidence of a coppice origin.

The front panel contains an average of 24 rings to the inch, as does the horizontal board on the top from which the lid hinges; both these boards are ornately carved by the same hand. The average across the deep back panel is between 10 and 11 rings to the inch; the maximum rate of growth however is 8. There are three internal drawers which also have this average ring density, one of the drawer dividers exhibits a very clear coppice sequence, see page 28. Apart from this and the one bottom board, all the oak in the desk came from open-grown trees. The lid was quarter-sawn and shows medullary rays.

All the carving on this desk is of a particularly high quality, especially the coiled dragon/vine leaf/grape decoration within the lozenge on the lid. It is likely that two craftsmen were responsible for the carving; the matting behind the dragon is finer than that in the background of the lunette panels. There is also some undercutting of the

129

vine leaves which gives them a three dimensional appearance; the sculptural effect of this carving is very similar to Church carving of an earlier period.

The lunette bands have the same punchwork decoration as those in box no. 19, a series of round beads running up the bands. Similarities in design, decoration, and the growth rate of the oak lead me to place this desk again somewhere in the English/Welsh border counties, although it does not do to rely too heavily on a Welsh source for the dragon; there are Gloucestershire chairs of the same period which carry the motif on their cresting rails; dragons lived further down in the West Country too.

One arm of the initial "T" crosses the marginal moulding of the lozenge, this was obviously added later. The barred "8" has baffled many people; the best suggestion is that it is a monogram of "E" and "B".

The lid moulding was made with a scratch-block with a shallow half-round section; however this is concave and not convex.

The joints are all rebated and nailed, the butterfly hinges are original but the lock is an 18th Century replacement.

The colour of the desk is a deep rich golden brown, with a very high patina.

I wonder whether the dragon is a temperance symbol; he lurks within the lozenge in a most sinister manner and he has a vine-leaf for a tail.

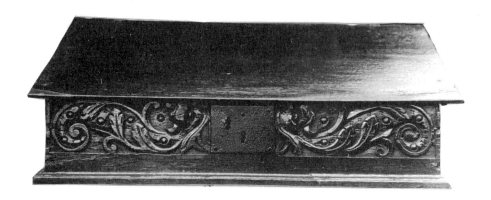

In common with many early pieces, this desk contains both sawn and cleft oak. The sawn panels are the sides and the front, which are about 3/4" thick, all the rest are cleft at about 1/4" thick; cleaving marks remain on the lower surfaces of the bottom boards. All the cleft panels show medullary rays quite strongly. The extra thickness of the front and sides not only gives the desk rigidity but allows for the very deep carving, also an early feature.

One of the sides has evidence of coppice growth, with a sequence of ten narrow rings sandwiched between two series of rapid increment; this board was almost quarter-sawn, whereas the other side was sawn tangentially. Whether sawn or cleft, the inner surfaces of all the panels have been scraped flat, there is no evidence of planing.

The fastest rate of growth in the desk is in the carved front panel, 15 years' growth made 3" of timber, or five rings to the inch. By the curvature of the annual rings, this timber came from a juvenile tree which was either a coppice shoot or a maiden tree growing free of competition. With evidence of coppice growth elsewhere in the desk, the former is the most likely.

There are strong Classical elements in the design on the front panel; the ancient "S" scroll has been developed to include acanthus-like foliage, and to terminate in a grotesque mask on each side of the lock plate. Here also

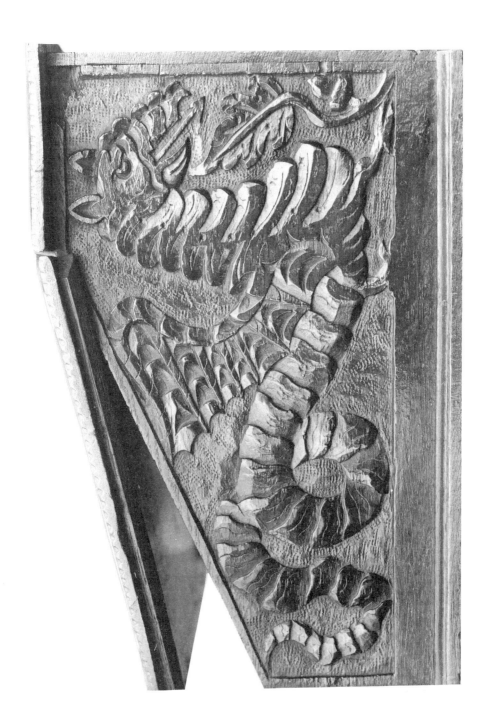

there are two carved pellets rather like footballs; these occur on many early 17th Century pieces. At least three different matting punches were employed to embellish the carving on the front panel.

The dragons on each side of the desk are identical and were probably copied by tracing. As on the front panel, the carving is deep and assured. These are pedigree winged dragons, with only two feet, and serpentine forked tongues. Furthermore I think that these must have been Westcountry dragons. The rate of growth of the timber in the desk is typically western, and the edges of the lid bear the characteristic chipped design seen on many Westcountry chests and boxes. The desk could also, of course, be Welsh, although in carved woodwork the Welsh did not have a monopoly of dragons.

The lid also bears traces of marginal decoration with scribed lines, although this is almost lost beneath the patina, which is very high. The colour is a rich deep brown. The lock plate and the flat fishtail hinges are original, but the moulding strip below the front panel is a replacement, made with a moulding plane in perhaps the 18th Century.

Dragon from 'Serpent and Dragon History, *Book II, 1540.'*
Copied by Edward Topsell in mid 17th century natural history books

134

Box no.23. Length 18½" Width 12½" Depth 8½"

c. 1620-1640

This little "country" box is made entirely from cleft oak averaging about 3/8" in thickness; rather weak medullary rays are present throughout. Growth rates vary from a maximum of 5 rings to the inch in the fastest sections to 16 rings in the slowest; all the panels show similar characteristics and almost certainly came from the same log. There are no signs of coppice rotations in the annual rings; the timber came from a tree that must have been free standing. With these growth rates it also came from an area of reasonably high rainfall.

The design of the front panel is a straight copy of one that appears on chests and chair backs over the period of about 1600-1630; it is not impossible that the box was made by some rural craftsman to match other furniture with the same design. There may be a clue to its origin in the leaf decoration along the top of the front panel; many Westcountry items carry this motif. The rate of growth of the timber is consistent with that in Somerset or Devon.

The initials "T.S." are contemporary with the rest of the carving, being made with the same "V" tool that formed the borders of the central motif beneath the lock plate.

The classical arches and the "S" curved motifs within them help to date the box, although the "S" scrolls with acanthus-like ends occur on

135

furniture over the whole of the first half of the 17th Century (see box no. 29).

The carver found less difficulty with the curves of the scrolls than with the outlines of the arches where mistakes are evident. Only two tools were employed, a "V" tool to make all the outlines of the design, and a single gouge to excavate the timber between the various elements. One feels that this is "in house" carving, it is obviously unskilled. Many "country" boxes are similarly carved, but not I feel to their detriment; they have a certain naive appeal.

The lid of the box has a simple incised marginal decoration composed of two scratched lines about 1/2" apart; the lid has no moulding whatsoever.

The lock and the hasp are original, the hinges are Victorian. Unfortunately these are broad and cover any evidence of earlier hinges. The box is a light brown colour, with a reasonable patina.

Box no.24.   Length 26½" Width 15½" Depth 8½"

c. 1620-1640

This handsome box has three separate timber identities. Firstly the front panel has very dense annual rings, in excess of 20 to the inch. Secondly the back board shows fairly fast growth at 7 rings to the inch. Lastly, the bottom boards have a very slow rate of growth at 26 rings to the inch. With such differing rates of growth each board must have come from a different tree.

The fine-textured oak in the front panel was obviously chosen by the carver in order to bear such crisp detail. As with some other carved front panels, this has been tangentially sawn. All the other panels are also of sawn oak; the lid, the back, and the bottom are all 3/8" thick, the sides and the front panel are 5/8". The timber for the lid, although not quarter sawn was chosen for an interesting grain pattern. The lid was made from two boards, the largest 12" wide. This board took the tree 102 years to make at an average of 8.5 years to the inch; it exhibits a gradual slowing of growth towards the end of this period. There are no signs of a coppice rotation in this board; it must have come from a free-standing tree which was perhaps slowing in growth towards middle age.

The lunette motif in the carving was extremely popular right up to the 1650's, indeed it has been held to be a sign of a mid-century piece. However, it appears on furniture of the late Elizabethan period as often as it does later on. Here the design within the lunettes is palmate; based on

138

the palm leaf. The overall design on this box is not dissimilar from that with interwoven lunettes on box no. 19. Here however the carver has enhanced the appearance of his work by chamfering the edges of the palm leaves within the bands, giving an almost three dimensional appearance to them; the angled surfaces were obviously intended to reflect the light.

The "atmosphere" of the carved design is wholly Mediterranean and must have appeared very exotic to the original owners. Why we think of these table boxes as English I do not know; hardly any have "English" motifs.

I feel that the lunette/palm leaf/acanthus combination together with the deep bottom moulding places the box between the suggested dates. I particularly like the floral decoration on the bottom moulding, intended to represent (I believe) lotus flowers.

The edges of the lid have a simple quadrant moulding cut with a plane. The sides of the box carry the same design as the front panel with the same craftsmanship in the carving; always the sign of a "quality" box.

The lock is original but the hasp is missing (as it so often is). The hinges are Victorian replacements; there is evidence that they were the third set fitted to the box. All the joints are rebated.

The box is a rich golden brown, with a very high patina.

German Woodcut c.1400.
This is St Christophers staff becoming a Date Palm after carrying Christ across a river

140

Box no.25.   Length 25" Width 16" Depth 8"

c.1620-1640

The finely carved box has a cleft top panel 16" in width which exhibits medullary rays; a good "figure" in the top panels was important as these surfaces were highly visible. This lid has strong evidence of a coppice origin, having a twenty-two year period of rapid growth between two periods of restricted. One of the other boards exhibits a thirty year period of dense growth between two sequences of broad annual rings. I doubt whether this board is from the same tree; the acceleration in growth after such a long period of suppression is more typical of the removal of a neighbour, probably in a wildwood situation. Over one section of the lid the tree achieved 5 rings to the inch, indicating a warm moist location. The carved front panel has dense even growth at 16 rings to the inch; hinting again at a deliberate choice of timber of this quality for carving purposes. All the timber in the box would appear to have been locally produced. The lid and the bottom boards are 1/4" thick, the other components of the box are just under 1/2". Apart from the lid, all the timber was sawn.

Mr. Dann, of Hatherleigh Antiques, near Okehampton, has told me that the design on the front panel of this box is not of leaves, but of the ears of wheat; this was a favoured motif of several Devon workshops during my suggested period. The configuration of the annual rings in the box is in accord with what one would expect of locally produced oak at the time, when natural oakwood stretched from Okehampton to Exeter; 5 rings to the inch would have been easily achieved by trees in the warm moist valleys, particularly if coppiced. The timber showing 16 rings to the inch may well have come from higher ground.

Wheat was grown in this part of Devon at the time, but apparently not thereafter, and it is interesting to find a fairly early box which does not have classical features on the front panel, although some acanthus leaf-tip decoration has crept in between the wheat-ears. On the side panels the maker reverted to a lunette motif, modified to fit the same basic curves as those on the front panel, but with a foliar insert; this is virtually identical with the lunette/foliar design on the panels in box no. 32.

The upper tip of the extreme right hand wheat-ear on the front panel is missing. To produce this the carving may have been cut from a longer length of prefabricated work. The section of the deep bottom moulding is typical of the suggested date; the top surface of the lid has scratch block moulding to type "D" page 64, this is only along the front edge. The lid also has punchwork decoration in the form of a shallow "S" between incised marginal lines.

The hinges are original, and of the flat fishtail variety. The lock and the hasp are 18th Century replacements.

The colour of the box is a deep brown, with a good patina.

All the panels in this little desk are of sawn material; only the carved front panel was quarter sawn, which in view of the carving (which obscures the medullary rays) seems superfluous. All the other boards are either cut tangentially, or at random. The back, bottom, and lid are 3/8" in thickness, the two side panels and the front are 5/8".

There is evidence of a 14 year coppice rotation in one of the side panels, otherwise the rest of the oak appears to have originated in a free-standing tree, the fastest rate of growth was about 10 rings to the inch.

The front panel in this desk is interesting in that in addition to the carving on the outside, it is also carved on the inner surface. The inside carving is very shallow and slightly different in design, it has proved impossible to photograph satisfactorily. The inner carving is obviously an abandoned attempt, but inexplicably the shallow ground is profusely matted, using the same punch as that employed on the outer carving. Why anyone should carry out such a tedious operation is beyond me, it was surely not necessary to practice matting with a punch. The inside work was almost certainly intended for this desk as it exactly fills the space available.

The vine and grape motif was a great favourite during the early Jacobean period, but I am not convinced that the designs on each side of the

lock plate are grapes. On the other hand the foliar extensions to the "S" scrolls look like vine leaves (see the better-carved examples on box no. 21). An alternative suggestion has been that these are pineapples, but I believe that these were not imported until the reign of Charles II. Perhaps the box is later after all, but it has other earlier features.

The lid bears scratch block moulding around all four sides, with the usual shallow half round section, the lower moulding was made by rounding-off the ends of the bottom boards.

All the metalwork is original apart from the screws securing the lock plate to the front panel.

The joints are rebated and nailed, the nails are quite large.

The desk is golden brown in colour, with a fair patina. When this desk came it was covered with a thick layer of Victorian varnish which fortunately came away easily by gently using the edge of a coin as a scraper; this revealed the original waxed surface which responded almost immediately to fresh polishing.

Length 21½" Width 13½" Depth 6½"

c. 1630-1640

All the panels in this little box were sawn; only the lid and the bottom board (surprisingly) were quarter sawn and display medullary rays. The lid and the bottom are 3/8" thick, all the other components of the box vary a little on each side of 1/2". The carved front panel is again tangentially sawn.

There is no evidence of a coppice source for the timber; growth in all the panels is reasonably steady at about 8 rings to the inch.

It is interesting to compare the carving on this box with that on the earlier box no. 10. The "S" scrolls are similar but those on box 10 are much finer, with a honeysuckle motif; the later box contains the more usual acanthus-leaf design. The carving on the later box is cruder in execution, with a minimum of punchwork decoration; taken all round, it is very "country-style" and as such is a very good example of an average country box of the period.

In style and execution this box is very similar the box no. 26 which is also constructed of sawn timber throughout; they are virtually contemporary. The surfaces of the acanthus fronds were originally further decorated by very slightly curved lines following the general curves of the design, these have almost disappeared beneath the patina. Almost identical decoration occurs on the fronds on the front panel of the desk,

147

more easily seen on the left-hand frond in the enlarged photograph.

Both this box and the desk share scratch-block moulding of the same profile on the lids; the bottom moulding in each case is formed by the front edge of the bottom boards, simply chamfered in the case of the box.

All the joints in the box are rebated and nailed.

The present hinges are of the round fishtail variety; originally there were ring hinges made simply of wire; the remnants of the earlier hinges still remain in the timber of the lid and the backboard.

The lock is a replacement, probably late 18th Century. The lock plate has the remains of a swinging cover above the key hole.

The box is a deep brown in colour, with a reasonable patina.

Box no.28.   Length 29" Width 16" Depth 9"

c. 1640-1660

The lid and bottom boards of this box are made of cleft oak, the front, sides, and back are all sawn. The cleft top is one single board 16" across showing vivid medullary rays across the whole surface; this timber took 86 years to make giving an average of 5.4 rings to the inch. This very fast rate of growth is fairly even across the whole width of the board and indicates that the tree must have grown in an area of high annual rainfall. There is no evidence of a coppice origin; the tree must have been free-standing for the whole of the period in which the timber was laid down. The end grain of the back panel has already been illustrated (page 24) and shows three narrower rings in each of two sequences.

The cleft boards are 3/8" thick, the sawn boards are a substantial 3/4". The thickness of the front and side panels, which are rebated and nailed together make this a very robustly constructed box.

The carved quatrefoil design on the front panel was a popular Westcountry motif, which could equate with the fast growth of the timber. Victor Chinnery, in his *Oak Furniture, the British Tradition* [*] illustrates two early 17th Century chests with similar designs. I believe that the small leaves within the quatrefoils are meant to represent oak

---

[*]   Published by Antique Collector's Club Ltd 1979.

leaves (in fact they look more like the leaves of the Turkey oak, but at this time it had not been introduced into Britain).

There is a similar front panel on a box in the Welsh Folk Museum which has the date 1721, but this is a later addition. (See box no. 54) It would not be surprising to find a box with this motif in Wales, there was considerable two-way traffic across the Bristol Channel in the 17th Century, the sea crossing being much quicker that the journey by road.

The Westcountry origin of the box might be further confirmed by the lining paper glued to the bottom of the box; this is a list of the Fairs and Markets for Hereford and the Border Counties for 1824. (There is also a window-tax schedule showing 6 windows).

There is a difference in the central motif in each quatrefoil which I do not understand. The carving is of a high quality and I do not believe that a craftsman able to work to this standard would make a mistake.

There is scratch block moulding around the edges of the lid which includes the shallow half-round section already seen on earlier boxes; this may put the date towards the earlier of my suggested dates. The two sequences of "dry-summer" rings would also put the box at about 1640, if this hypothesis is valid.

The highly decorative and unusual lock plate is original; I have seen this on other furniture from about 1630 to 1650. The box is a rich brown colour, with a high patina.

Box no.29.　　　　　Length 48" Width 14" Height 21"

c. 1630-1650

All the oak in this chest is home-grown, of the apparently standard 3/4" thickness. None of the boards was quarter-sawn. The fastest rate of growth is about 6 rings to the inch. The back board has a period of even growth followed by a gradual slowing down over a fifty year period. This was followed by a 25 year period of very slow growth, after which there is a sudden increase to a larger annual increment. These periods are probably too long to give a coppice source for the timber; the sequence of slow growth rings must have occurred when the tree encountered competition and I suggest that the tree was one of a group in a wood-pasture or wildwood situation. A thinning operation would have produced the later increase in growth; alternatively, removal of one of the outside trees in a group, perhaps to extend pasture, would have had the same effect.

All the boards in the chest show some gradual slowing down in the growth rate; several show 6 rings to the inch at the beginning of the sequence.

An unusual feature in the carving is the ropework strip running between the lunette band and the lower "S" scroll decoration. This rope moulding can be found on capitols of the Norman period and in furniture decoration is I believe a Gloucestershire motif. If this is so, the rate of growth of the timber is consistent with a Westcountry tree from an area of reasonably high rainfall; trees from fertile sites in the Severn plain can exhibit this rate of growth, as do those from the remaining wood-pasture in the Forest of Dean.

The length of this chest gives it a certain elegance. The decoration is the fairly standard combination of palmate lunettes and "S" scrolls used extensively in furniture of the period. I favour the earlier of my dates, the lid has the older shallow half round moulding in a strip running along the top surface at the front.

The lock and the hasp are original, the hinges are a replacement. The original long strap hinges have left their mark in the form of nail holes on the backboard.

Most of the 16th and 17th Century chests which I have seen have heights varying between about 20" to 22"; this is about the same as those of joint stools and benches of the period. I do not believe that this is coincidental; one can comfortably sit on a 20" chest.

Box no.30.　　　　　Length 27½" Width 15½" Depth 6½"

c.1650-1660

All the panels in this box are of sawn oak. The front and sides are 5/8", the bottom and back boards are 3/8" and the front is 1/2" thick. All the timber is home-grown, with a maximum growth rate of 6 rings to the inch. All the boards are straight-grained, none show medullary rays. The front board has a series of narrow rings between two periods of rapid growth and shows the sudden increase in increment after a restricted period consistent with coppice cutting or a thinning operation. The wider boards do not show this sequence, growth is steady. If all the boards came from the same tree this probably grew in a wood-pasture group where a competing tree was removed. There is a group of "dry summer" rings in this box.

All the surfaces of the timber in this box show the marks of a finishing plane the blade of which had been ground to a very shallow concave profile.

The simple decoration was made by only two tools, a "V" tool, and a gouge with a diameter of about 1/2". This latter tool took out the main features of the design and also produced the notches on the sides of the front panel. A simple star-shaped punch was used to fill in the vacant spaces on the side panels, which carry the same design as the front.

The austerity of the design of this box probably puts it at pre-Restoration, although it is lined with paper bearing a "Four Seasons" block print with the Arms of the Haberdashers Company, and this would

not be earlier that 1689. If the box was lined at manufacture I am quite wrong about the date, but the box has a distinctly Puritan look about it; also, the channel moulding running along the lower part of the front panel was made with a scratch block.

I have not found this particular decoration upon another box, although something very like it occurs on furniture from the Salisbury, Wiltshire area. I would like to think that it represents the Christian "fish" symbol, in which case this may well be truly a "Bible" box. The shallow depth would have easily accommodated the Bibles of the period.

All the joints are rebated, and nailed. The nails are small (which can be a late feature).

The hinges are of the "round fishtail" variety and are original, as is the lock.

The box is a rich red-brown, with a good patina.

The link with the Haberdasher's Company is interesting, I have two boxes with this paper. Even today shops wrap purchases in paper bearing their "Logo" if not their name, and in the 17th Century, when paper was probably scarce it is very likely that a housewife would use such wrapping paper to line the box in which she kept such purchases, perhaps gloves or other small items of millinery.

Box no.31.   Length 24" Width 17" Depth 10"

Dated 1674

Unusually for a box of this late date, all the panels are of cleft oak. Even the two bottom boards display medullary rays, on the outside of the front panel these are lost within the carving. The characteristic partial splitting of the grain on the surface of the boards is present on surfaces within the box. The front and back panels are 3/4" thick, the sides, the top, and the bottom are all 1/2". Rebated joints give the box a very solid construction.

There is no evidence of a coppice origin for any of the timber in the box; the maximum rate of growth is between six and seven rings to the inch. The two boards which make up the lid are quite different in ring-density, with a minimum of twenty rings to the inch over both 8" widths; this is almost certainly imported timber. In addition, the medullary rays on these boards are less prominent than on the others. The home-grown timber has a ring-density consistent with it having come from a free growing tree which never encountered competition. Across the 9" width of the front panel there are 82 annual rings, an average of 9 to the inch; this board gradually slows in growth from one side to the other.

About 65 years down on the front panel is a group of three dry-summer rings; allowing a possible two inches of sapwood which would have been discarded, this allows perhaps 83 years back from the date of the box to the end of the dry period. Three consecutive dry-summer years ended in

159

1592. 1674 minus 83 years is 1591; for what it is worth.

Most of the boxes from 1650 onwards seem to average about 10" deep; this is no exception. Indeed one sign of a later box could well be that it should be more than 9" in depth. Apart from the carved design, this box has other late features; the nails which secure the boards are slender, and the boards themselves have been worked to even thicknesses. Inside and out, the boards are of a very dark reddish colour which may have an atmospheric cause, but could also be the result of staining to compete with imported mahoganies.

The tulips in the carving are an immediate clue to the date; these are almost invariably late-century, at any rate post Restoration. The central motif of four joined fleur-de-lis occurs frequently on furniture of the period; easily worked with one gouge it must have been a convenient filler. It also occurs on one panel of the earlier Westcountry box no. 28, as does the zig-zag marginal decoration on the lid of the later box.

The pomegranate motifs on the front panel are interesting; the Ashmolean Museum has similar fruit on blackwork wallpapers of the late 17th century. Pomegranates have a biblical significance, they were the fruit given by Eve to Adam (not apples, as commonly held).

All the ironwork in the box has been replaced. The colour is a deep reddish brown, with a high patina.

(Ashmolean Museum)

This desk was constructed from sawn oak. The lid is a single board 18" wide and 1/2" thick, quarter sawn to show the medullary rays. The back, sides and front are all 5/8" thick but these boards are not quarter sawn, in view of the amount and depth of carving this would not have been necessary.

There is evidence of a coppice origin across the width of the lid, there are two fifteen year periods of rapid growth sandwiched between periods of slower; the maximum rate of growth is in the back board; at 5 rings to the inch this just precedes a period of slower growth. The curvature of the annual rings in this board indicates that it was cut from very near the centre of a very young tree, perhaps in the early years of a first rotation in a recently coppiced area. A similar fast rate of growth is present in the annual rings of the carved front panel.

All the timber in this desk was obviously locally-produced and almost certainly came from the same source, if not from the same tree.

The characteristics of the timber in this desk are virtually identical with those of the timber in box no. 25 although the latter came from an open situation. Each has grown at a maximum rate of 5 rings to the inch

The carving is of a particularly high standard in each, as is the workmanship as a whole and I believe that they might well have been

162

163

made in the same area, particularly as they share a common design (on the side panels of box no. 25 and on the front of this desk.)

The punch decoration on the box and the desk also share common forms. Both have punchwork in the shape of a small four-bladed propeller (or perhaps a flower); dotted curves of various radii are common to both. In addition each has an oblong punchmark consisting of eight small squares, used to matt the ground.

The absence of scratch block moulding in the desk and the introduction of a tulip motif into the decoration make it later than the box, and a post-Restoration date is indicated.

The internal lock is interesting; the present one is Victorian and I believe that originally the desk may have had no lock at all. There are no signs of a previous internal lock and no nail or screw holes on the rear of the front panel.

The colour of this desk is a rich deep brown, with a high patina. The original hinges were flat fishtails, now replaced by brass Victorian butt hinges.

Box no.33. Length 30½" Width 17½" Depth 11½"

c.1660-1680

All the timber in this large box is sawn, each panel is a uniform 1/2" thick, The lid has been made from one board 17½" wide; this was radially sawn from near the centre of a large log and shows medullary rays. This board has a definite coppice-with-standards pedigree and shows evidence of having been produced over the first few rotations of a coppiced area. The tree grew to about 9" diameter at a maximum growth rate of 7 rings to the inch and then slowed considerably for about 5 years as the underwood caught up with it. Following removal of this the tree grew rapidly for a further 25 years before competition again slowed the growth, for perhaps another ten years, after which it resumed a more rapid growth rate again. The average rate of growth over the most typical section of this board was 9.2 rings to the inch.

This average compares with the earlier similarly decorated box no. 19, which was 8.8 rings to the inch. This earlier box was also made of timber with a coppice origin, and it may well be that the two boxes shared the same county of origin, somewhere along the English/Welsh border. It is perhaps coincidental that both boxes are extremely deep.

The major difference in decoration is that the later box has three complete arches, whereas the earlier, being shorter, has one. Each box has modified acanthus decoration within the lunette bands. Each box has

165

coppice-grown timber.

There is a primitive appeal to the carving which it would lack if the design were less bold; the "V" tool has been extensively employed and traces all the major elements in the design; a single gouge has simply chipped out details within the main decoration, which was subsequently enhanced by the use of a small star-shaped punch

A strong clue to date lies in the moulding of the lid and that below the carved front panel. The lid moulding is meagre and is to section "J" on page 64. The bottom moulding is ogee which was planted on top of the bottom boards, which protrude sufficiently to form the bottom step of the moulding. Both were produced with a moulding-plane. On the earlier boxes with a bottom moulding this lower step is usually an integral part of the strip of wood which formed the moulding.

The box is a typical example of a "country" piece imitating an earlier style and a straight comparison with the earlier box is instructive.

The joints are all rebated and nailed; the nails are small. All the metalwork is original, but the hasp is missing. The colour of the box is a blackish-red, and may have been stained at manufacture.

The patina is good. This is the deepest box in the sample and one wonders again about bonnets; this was surely big enough to contain them.

167

This is another box made entirely of sawn oak; the front, the sides, and the back are all 5/8", the lid is 1/2" thick, and all the bottom boards are 1/4". The maximum growth rate in the timber is a very fast 4.5 rings to the inch indicating growth in a fertile warm high rainfall area. The box displays medullary rays on the top surface of the lid and the front panel. Two boards make up the lid, the largest at 12½" wide took only 57 years to produce, an average of 4.56 rings to the inch across the whole width of the board, which shows an even growth rate throughout the period. There are no signs of a coppice origin anywhere in the timber and the parent tree must have been free-standing in a particularly favourable location. (Park trees will produce similar growth).

All the joints are rebated, and nailed together. An odd feature in this box is the way in which the side panels are joined to the front; instead of the front panel overlapping the sides, the opposite occurs. The advantage of this is that the nails are not visible from the front as they are driven into the end-grain of the front panel from the sides. The disadvantage is that the end-grain of the side panels is visible from the front. This arrangement occurs in some later boxes, where applied half-round moulding disguises the end grain.

The lid originally hinged on wooden dowels protruding from the ends of

the back board. These fitted into holes drilled through substantial battens which were nailed beneath the lid on each side. This must have been a useful device for country workshops which might have run out of the metal variety; no doubt it was also cheaper.

The bold strapwork in this box gives it a much earlier appearance and the design of the front panel could well belong to the first quarter of the century. However, like other motifs in country districts it lingered on; in some northern counties strapwork appears on dated court cupboards as late as 1680; I have even seen it on a dated piece of 1722. In this box the presence of moulding-plane work (to section "J" on the lid) makes it later.

The colour of this box is similar to that of the preceding one, and I suspect that here again this is original and not the product of age. Many of these boxes must have been stained in order to compete with imported timbers, particularly at this date. I can see no other reason why some later boxes are darker in colour than the earlier ones, some have distinctly red hues.

I have seen a Cornish box with the same strapwork pattern of similar date; this had a known local history. It also had concave bottom moulding, but rather deeper in section. Certainly, this box could exhibit a Cornish rate of growth; sheltered valleys in the south of the county would produce such timber.

Box no.35.　　　　Length 28" Width 15½" Depth 10"

c. 1680-1700

All the panels in this box show prominent medullary rays, and all are of sawn oak. The front and sides are 1/2" thick, the other boards are 3/8". All have been planed to a precise thickness, there is none of the random variation found in early boxes. There is a precision in the workmanship as if the maker was having to compete with better made furniture, as indeed he might have been during this period, when chests of drawers were ousting the traditional table boxes.

A well defined coppice-with-standards sequence occurs in the progression of the annual rings on the back board; this shows 15 years of slow growth followed by 25 of fast, followed by a further 20 years of slow growth succeeded by yet another period of fast, ending at the edge of the board. The front panel is of more even growth, averaging 10 rings to the inch over a 9" width of timber; again the finer timber seems to have been deliberately chosen for the carved panel. The timber in the box almost certainly came from two sources, one from a standard tree in a coppiced area, the other from a free-standing tree.

The decoration is interesting, being a heady mixture of the old and the new; the round floral motifs have a geometric appearance in keeping with the philosophy of the end of the century, but they are a development of a Renaissance form. The branched floral design beneath the lock plate is

171

more in keeping with decoration such as that on box no. 40; here is another use of the tulip.

The bottom moulding again is meagre and of a late form, being made with a moulding plane, the lid however has something very like scratch block moulding.

The standard of workmanship in this box makes it anything but a "country" piece; the carving is crisp and full of detail,

All the joints are rebated and secured by small nails (perhaps with better furniture being produced in quantity, smaller nails would have become more easily available.)

The lock plate is not original but merely covers the hole made by the original lock which is missing. The hinges are original, of the flat "fishtail" variety.

This is a very commodious box and could well have accommodated anything which might otherwise have found a home in the lower part of a chest of drawers; many of the later boxes are quite large and may have been made with this in mind. Again, the box is a reddish brown in colour, with a good patina.

All the panels in this box are of sawn oak. The lid and the front panel have been finished to 1/2" thick, the side and back panels are 3/8". The bottom has two boards with the joints running back to front, these boards are also 1/2" thick. Only the lid has medullary rays, and was thus quarter-sawn.

The lid is formed from one board 16½" wide; one wonders why with timber of this dimension to hand the maker needed to use two boards to make the bottom of the box. The are 90 annual rings across the width of the lid, making an average rate of growth of 5.45 rings the the inch. This growth rate is very even, indicating a free-standing tree which never encountered competition, either from other oaks, or from coppice regrowth around it. The fastest growth-rate is about 4 rings to the inch; the tree from which this timber was cut must have stood in a very favourable location, on a fertile site with a high average rainfall and long warm growing seasons. Such rates of growth can be achieved on less favourable sites during the very early years of a coppice-grown oak when, following the felling of trees of substantial size, the stumps of the old trees produce coppice shoots which for a while are fed by the widespread root-system of the parent stump. Under these circumstances, however, after perhaps thirty years or so, the rapid growth rate ceases abruptly due to

competition from neighbouring stems or regrowth from other species. The lid of this box shows no evidence of such deceleration in growth.

The date is contemporary with the box, having been carved with the same "V" tool which excavated virtually all the other main elements in the design. The tool has been used to sketch the pattern in the surface of the wood, leaving this mostly intact. (Earlier carving relied for its effect upon the removal of most of the surface of the wood, leaving a design that was almost sculptured.) Within the lunettes on this box, the only major removal of timber was on each side of the vertical stem, otherwise the design was strengthened simply by the use of a large gouge which emphasised the ends of the scrolled decoration within the lunettes. This method of decoration is very much of the late 17th/early 18th Century. Other late features are: the finishing of the various panels which make up the box into uniform thicknesses, the use of small-headed nails, and the planed moulding around the lid.

The notched end-grain at each end of the front panel appears on many West-country pieces of furniture, as does the treatment of the design within the lunettes, where the central vertical stem is heavily buttressed.

The metalwork in the box is all original, including the unusual ornamental lock-plate, which appears to be a blundered version of an earlier pattern. All the joints are rebated. The colour is a chocolate-brown, with a high patina.

Box no.37.   Length 27" Width 18" Depth 10"

c. 1680-1700

This box is integral with a stand. The sides, back and bottom are all of elm, only the lid and the front panel are of oak. These are both 3/8" thick and are of sawn timber; there are tooth-marks from a pit-saw on the inner surfaces of each board. Two boards make up the lid, but only one has been quarter-sawn, this shows medullary rays and exhibits a long period of steady growth at about 6 rings to the inch, culminating in a period of suppressed growth. The front panel shows an even faster rate of growth, with a maximum of 5 rings to the inch, but there is no evidence of a coppice origin. The elm board ends are tucked away inside the other panels and it is not possible to examine the end-grain, but examination of the surfaces shows extremely rapid growth, which is not unusual for this species, particularly on fertile sites in a high rainfall area. These elm boards are 1/2" thick, which is necessary to give the box rigidity in view of the rather thin oak panels.

All the oak is home-grown. The baluster turning of the legs of the stand is typical of the late 17th/early 18th Century and as the stand is original, (and not a later addition, as so many are) this helps to date the box. There is no moulding around the lid, but there is a marginal decoration comprising two parallel incised lines. The lower moulding is made with a moulding plane.

The decoration of the front panel is in very low relief, the excavated portion is only some 1/8" deep, and virtually all the design was accomplished by the "V" tool.

The primitive design on the front panel has a child-like simplicity; the stylised tulips also indicate a late date. The initials "S.C." although off-centre and of different size are original and were cut with the same tool that took out the rest of the design.

The stand contains mortice and tenon joints which are all well made; the joints in the box, surprisingly, are not rebated, but simply butted and nailed. Again, the nails are small and neat.

This style of carving, where quite large areas of the original surface of the wood are kept untouched as part of the design can be found on many small items of furniture of the period. One wonders whether such crude work would have sold earlier in the century.

The box has flat "fishtail" hinges which are original, as is the lock.

The patina is high, the colour of the oak panels is a deep chocolate; the elm boards have developed that golden russet colour which is typical of the timber after many years of polishing.

I include this somewhat simple chest because it has some history, it was privately bought from a farm near Tintern Abbey, from a family whose forebears had farmed the land since the 17th Century. It had lived unused in a cellar for as long as anyone could remember. It must have been a few inches higher originally, there is considerable erosion on the parts in contact with the ground, as one would expect from long internment in a wet cellar which occasionally flooded.

The oak boards in this chest are substantial; the back is 1" thick, all the other boards are 7/8". Here again is a uniformity in the thickness of finished timber which seems to be characteristic of later pieces. If this is genuinely a Lower Wye Valley chest, the timber almost certainly came from the Forest of Dean. The tree ring evidence is that of a free standing tree with no sign of a coppice origin; most of the boards show a reasonably

steady rate of growth. The fastest-growing section of timber shows about 5 rings to the inch as a maximum. The front board is tangentially sawn and gives about 15 rings to the inch, again as if it had been deliberately chosen for a finer grain. Being so sawn it is only possible to estimate the rate of growth, it is possible that the rest of the log from which the board came was completely different. The most that one could say is that this particular piece of timber came from the outer parts of a tree which was slowing considerably in growth because of overcrowding, or simply old age.

The average rate of growth of one of the side boards is 11" in 82 years, or 7.4 rings to the inch.

One indication of a late date for the chest is the internal lock which I believe to be original, although there is puzzling evidence of an original strap beneath the lid, at the locking point. This does not coincide with anything on the front panel, yet there never was a frontal lock as there is no excavation to accept it on the panel. The likeliest explanation is that the lid was at some time replaced, but this does not explain the notch cut in the top of the front panel above the lock. (This could possibly have been caused during an attempt to force the lock, however.)

The lip of the lid has a flattened quadrant-shaped moulding and there is a half-round moulding running along the bottom of the front panel, both are very uniform and were cut with a moulding plane.

All the joints are butted and nailed, the substantial hinges are the second set.

There is a till on the left hand side of the interior, in this I found the remains of tallow candle-wax.

The colour of the timber is a muddy grey-brown, with no patina whatsoever.

Box no.39.   Length 27" Width 12" Depth 8"

Dated 1711

Whoever made this box was short of large-dimensioned timber. Although only 12" wide, the top and the bottom are each made from two boards, neatly dowelled together. The top is only 3/8" thick, and the joint is made by four hardwood dowels no more than 1/8" in diameter; the strap hinges straddle the joint and help to hold the lid together. One of the dowels in the bottom has broken out of the timber, the drilled hole is 5/8" deep.

The boards of the lid appear to be of cleft oak, the rest of the timber in the box was sawn. Coarse pit-saw marks remain on the underside of one of the bottom boards; some of these show the saw advancing 1/4" or more with each stroke, which leads me to conclude that log from which the boards was cut was of small diameter. Deep saw-marks on other panels indicate that the saw had a very wide "set".

The two side panels are about 1" thick at the bottom, at the top they have been chamfered to a thickness of 1/2" to match that of the front and back panels. These side panels have been rebated into the carved front panel and have been set back 1/2" from the edges of this board. Thus, although from the front the lid does not appear to overlap, it extends over the sides by this amount. This overlapping of the front panel is unusual and may be a regional feature. Gabriel Olive illustrates a coffer dated 1642 in his article on West Country chests, coffers and boxes in "Regional Furniture" (1990) with this feature; both the coffer and this box also have scalloped end-grain on the front panel.

It is difficult to determine the rate of growth of the oak in this box, due to the blocking of the end-grain of the panels with dirt and polish, but the inner surface of the lid shows a very rapid decrease in growth at one point; the widest obvious ring in the box is only 1/8" wide, and generally the average ring width is much less than this. For this reason I doubt whether the timber is of West Country origin; if it is, the tree was standing in an unfavourable location.

The box is an odd mixture of "rustic" and professional, certainly it took some skill to accurately dowel the lid and the bottom boards; this does not equate with the crude cutting and finishing of the two side panels. The carving of the front panel is of a high standard; here again there is a mixture of motifs which is odd. The initials, the date, and the floral elements are very 18th Century, similar work can be found on samplers. The lower carving of strapwork scrolls could well be a hundred years earlier, if it were not for the elaborate use of the "V" tool to embellish the design.

The box is a deep brown, with a high patina.

Another deep "bottom-drawer" type of box, this one also has timber planed to an equal thickness throughout, all the boards except the lid are 1/2", the lid is 3/8". All the timber is sawn, and all is home-grown. The oak shows an extremely rapid rate of growth; the bottom boards exhibit 4 rings to the inch, one board grew at this rate over 8". None of the boards was quarter sawn, and I believe this to have been deliberate as the timber is a deep red colour, which must have been produced by staining, and such colouring would have made it pointless to use expensive boards showing a medullary ray as this would have been hidden beneath the stain.

The tree which produced such a rapid rate of growth must have lived in a very favourable environment, on a deep fertile loam in a warm sheltered position, in an area with a high rainfall; it could perhaps have been a tree which was growing beside a stream, or in a valley bottom with a high water table. The coastal strip of South Wales could in places produce these conditions, and there may be a further clue to the source of the timber in the carved design on the front panel of the box. The Welsh Folk Museum has a coffre-bach with a floral design in the same manner, (see box 51) where the petals of the predominant flowers are deeply gouged into the timber of the front panel, to a greater depth than the flat field of the carving. This must surely be a regional practice. In addition, the round devices on the front panel have a hint of the round berry inlays

found on some boxes of the period from the Vale of Glamorgan.

There is an appealing rustic confidence in the carving of this panel, which is extremely well executed. The field is quite deep and considerable effort must have gone into the removal of so much wood; many hours must also have been spent in matting the background with a punch.

Tulips are again a strong element in the design, presented in profile as on box no. 37.

The lid has a narrow ogee moulding running only along the front edge; this was produced with a moulding plane. The sides of the lid have a simple decoration of fine notching, as do the sides of the front panel.

All the joints are butted and secured by fine nails; I would not be surprised if they were also glued.

The lock is the original, as are the round "fishtail" hinges.

The colour of the box is a deep mahogany red, with a very high patina. The colour is consistent with the use of red ochre as a finish, although I believe that in some parts of Wales, ox blood was used for this purpose.

Box no.41.　　　　Length 23" Width 13" Depth 8½"

c. 1700-1720

The thickness of all the panels in this box is a uniform 1/2". The lid, which is one board of 13" width, is quarter sawn, but the medullary rays are almost invisible due to the deep colour of the patina.

The carved front panel and the sides have ring densities of between 17 and 20 to the inch; the lid shows a gradual reduction in ring width from a maximum of 5 to 12 to the inch across the board, the average is 10.

There is no evidence of a coppice source for any of the timber in the box; the ring sequence in the lid indicates a free-standing location. The later slower growth in this board indicates a tree slowing in growth due to age, growing on a slightly less fertile site than that which produced the preceding box. The front panel appears again to have been chosen for a finer grain.

The bottom board is a single piece of pine 1/4" thick, but this is not original as it has been secured by fairly modern screws. Signs of earlier nail holes are obscured by the pine board.

The lid of the box has moulding of the same section as the previous one, made by a plane.

The design of the front panel has much in common with the Welsh coffre-bach already mentioned; the flowers sprout from a vase-shape in a similar fashion, but the petals are not so deeply set. The carving of the panel demonstrates a certain skill, it is not the work of a "country" carver.

189

The carpentry too is of a high standard, the joints are well dovetailed and fit precisely; for added security some of these joints are secured by small nails, the heads of which have been punched to just below the surface of the timber.

Compared with the earlier 17th Century boxes, this one looks almost modern. It was of course produced for a much more sophisticated market and had to sell in competition with furniture made from the more highly coloured imported timbers; it does in fact have the colour of "plum pudding" Cuban mahogany. The patina is so high that I suspect that it may have originally been varnished. This would have been the opportunity for the maker to introduce colour.

The lock plate is original, but the hasp is missing. The original hinges were of the ring type, but they have been replaced by fairly modern butt hinges, screwed into place. (There should be some way of dating a box by the number of sets of hinges it has had. Some of the earlier boxes have had three sets.)

191

Length 23" Width 14" Depth 10"

c. 1720-1740

Many of these later boxes appear to be 10" deep; this must have been a popular size.

The lid and the front panel of this box are of quarter sawn timber; here again the medullary rays are almost lost in the deep colour. The lid and bottom boards are of 3/8" thickness, the other boards are 5/8". All have been planed to a uniform thickness.

There is no evidence of coppice growth in any of the timber in the box; variations in ring width are typical of an open grown tree. The front panel is of very straight grain, but shows a gradual deceleration in growth from about 10 rings to the inch to 30 or more, which would indicate that the boards were probably cut from a tree of quite large size, slowing as it passed maturity. The fastest growth in the box is 10 rings to the inch, indicating a locality of low annual rainfall.

The carving on the front panel is of a high quality, with a slightly sculptural look to the laurel leaves. Otherwise, the design is in low relief with a complete absence of matting in the ground of the field. This lack of matting gives the panel a distinctly "vacant" look; undoubtedly, matting serves to accentuate the higher points of a design. At first sight, the two halves of the design appear to be mirror images, but on closer inspection this is not so, possibly the leaves were drawn free-hand and not from a template.

The laurel leaves are no clue to the date of the box, the shrub was a popular introduction to gardens in the 16th and 17th Centuries; one variety preceding the other.

There is no moulding anywhere on the box; the edges of the lid and base boards are simply chamfered.

The lock is the original, and is secured by screws with quite coarse threads. The hasp is a modern reproduction.

The box is a deep mahogany red, the patina is very high, perhaps indicating, as in the previous box, the use of a varnish by the maker.

Box no.43.　　　　　　Length 28½" Width 16" Depth 9"

Dated 1719

All the boards which make up this box are a uniform 1/2" in thickness; all are of sawn timber. The lid and carved front panel are quarter sawn, both show medullary rays although these have been almost obliterated in the front panel by the use of a matting punch. The lid and the bottom have each been made from two boards which have a tongued-and-grooved joint between; the first use of this device in any of the boxes.

On one of the two top boards, the tree took 79 years to make 10" of timber, an average growth rate of 7.9 rings to the inch. Growth across this board is very regular, with no sign of a coppice source for the timber. The carved front panel shows a similar rate of growth at 8.2 rings to the inch over an 8" width. From the evidence in the annual rings, the parent tree was an isolated one, in a wood-pasture or perhaps a hedgerow situation. There is no sign of a slowing of growth anywhere in the box. The average rate of growth of this box is slightly dissimilar to that in the previous Welsh boxes; the maximum rate is about the average. If the box is also Welsh, which seems likely from the design of the flowers on the front panel, the tree obviously came from a slightly less favoured location.

The design on the front panel contains yet again the deeply-gouged petals of the flowers which form the main features; it is useful to find a dated example of this motif, possibly confirming the period of other boxes which share the same design. These deep petals are the only part of the design where a gouge was used, all the other elements were taken out with a "V" tool, as were the initials and the date. There was no attempt to excavate a ground, the punch marks which comprise the matting are scattered rather carelessly over the surface of the oak.

The lid has moulding to section "J" on page 64, made with a moulding plane. The bottom boards are simply rounded off.

The use of vertical half-round moulding strips on each side of the front is interesting, perhaps this was an attempt to compete with the more fashionable chests of drawers of the period, which would have carried the same moulding, although bearing in mind the desperately poor quality of the carving perhaps they needn't have bothered.

The joints in the box are all butted and nailed; the nails are again small.

When the box came it was lined with a rather dirty green paper; removal of this led to the surprising discovery of some delightful ink-and-wash drawings of country scenes, unhappily too foxed and damaged to resurrect, although I was able to save a cherub who now graces the end-plate of this book.

The box shows signs of long neglect in the poor, faded colour, and almost complete lack of patina.

Length 32½" Width 21" Height 11"

c. 1700-1720

This large desk is constructed throughout of sawn oak of 1/2" thickness. The sides and the narrow front panel show medullary rays and were quarter sawn. The only reasonably visible length of end-grain is in the back panel, one of the boards of which shows an even rate of growth over some 8½".

Unfortunately the end grain of the lid, which is one board 15" wide, in completely hidden by the moulded beading planted on either side. The grain on the surface of the lid however shows what appears to be two periods of restricted growth perhaps 65 years apart; this interval is too long for the timber to have a normally-managed coppice source, or to be a period between thinning operations. The tree grew rapidly between the two periods of restricted growth and for this period of its life it must have been free-standing; there is a possibility that the first slow period was caused at the very end of an old coppice rotation, after which the oak had managed to put its crown well above the competition. If the standard trees on the old coppice area had been left at a very wide spacing, it might take 65 years for them to touch, causing the second period of slow growth. In view of all this, it is safer to allot an open source for the timber.

The top and bottom mouldings of the desk carry on around all four sides, it was obviously meant to be seen from all directions. All the mouldings, top and bottom, were produced by a moulding plane.

The row of Doric columns is an interesting feature and give the desk an early appearance, but this is belied by the general "finish" and the uniform thickness of the timber.

Internally the desk has well-fitted shelves and drawers; it was obviously made for an office. Originally the desk was fitted with an external lock and corresponding hasp; the present internal lock is probably Victorian. The hinges are original, of a stubby "fishtail" variety.

There is little patina, as one would expect with a commercial desk which would have been dusted but hardly ever polished. In consequence, the colour is a rather dull brown. The top surface of the lid has at some time been blackened. The maker branded his initials (R.B.) into the lower side of the lid.

Dating an item such as this is very difficult. At first sight it looks very early, but it has many late features in common with other boxes of the period.

In all of the preceding 44 chests desks, and boxes I have been able to give details of their timber content and in some cases, possible sources; in the following section I illustrate a random sample of a few boxes which for one reason or another are also interesting in other ways.

Box no.45.   Length 11" Width 7¾" Depth 6"

Dated 1795 but probably 17th Century

The "carving" on this little box was done with the point of a knife; note the irregularity of the more curved lines. Had this been done before the box had been assembled, the effect would have been better; the carver would have had far more control over the tool if the panel had been lying flat on a bench. It is almost impossible to accurately carve a panel once it has been made into a box.

The box has a glass-like patina and a deep red colour; this, the ring hinges, and the lock have persuaded me that it was made perhaps a hundred years before "S.B." spent an afternoon scratching his initials into it.

I have no details of this little box, which is about the same size as the previous example. I illustrate it because of the bottom moulding, which places it at about the same date as box no. 30. This one too has a distinctly "Puritan" atmosphere.

(Courtesy of Combe Cottage Antiques)

I include this little desk because it taught me a lesson that I should have learned long ago. It was cheap, therefore I bought it. Bargains admittedly do occur, but so seldom these days that should one come along, it is worth standing back for a while before reaching for the cheque book. As it was inexpensive, I do not have really bad feelings about the desk; I knew in the shop that there was something odd about it, but as it was wearing about an eighth of an inch of Victorian varnish I reasoned that a good clean would reveal the original desk and I was prepared to ignore certain nagging doubts, particularly as the dealer sliced a hefty chunk from the asking price in the course of negotiations.

If one pretends to be a serious collector the first consideration when faced with a possible purchase should be authenticity; is it all original? Is every part of it correct for the period? With desks and table boxes, the answer is usually yes; it has hardly ever been worthwhile for anyone to indulge in creative restoration; odd hinges and locks have been replaced of course, but this is wear and tear and can sometimes prove authenticity.

In the event, the only authentic parts of this desk turned out to be the carved front and side panels; all the rest was added at a later date. Just how much later I do not know, but I suspect that he who applied the varnish has much to answer for. On the other hand, given a few pieces of what had been a very nice table box of about 1630, give or take a decade, and the choice of either abandoning them or making something useful, who can blame him?

The bottom boards are two cut-down panels from a coffer (quite obvious when I got it home and up-ended the desk; why didn't I spot this in the shop?) The two triangular panels above the carved side panels are slightly thinner than the boards beneath them. The lid is made of oak with a very, very slightly different texture that that in the original panels; with the varnish removed it is too smooth. The backboard must be a replacement as it occupies the whole of the back; the original would have only been as tall as the lower panels. The lower moulding is an obvious replacement (although in all fairness I did spot this in the shop) The notched decoration of these strips was done with the same small gouge as that on the upper side panels and the lid; the "feel" of this later carving is quite different than that of the early work, and I really should have spotted this, despite the varnish.

I once bought (again cheaply) a Jacobean bench which was perfect in every respect apart from the band-saw marks beneath the apron; this I kept as a reminder of how easily it is to fool oneself. This little desk is in the same category, but I quite like it. It has a slightly self-conscious look as if apologising for what has happened to it.

Box no.48.   Length 24½" Width 17" Height 10"

Dated (?) 1662

This desk is not in the same category as box no. 47, but it presents several enigmas which are interesting. Although at first sight it looks all of a piece, closer examination reveals a puzzling history. The lid is of cleft oak, but is a replacement. The top fixed board from which it hinges has the older scratch block moulding; this does not match the lid which has only a carved marginal decoration. The original hasp mounting position on the lid was above the left-hand 6 in the date. The present hinges are of brass, but there are signs of original butterfly hinges under the fixed top board; the nail holes are still present, in the correct position. The lower surface of the lid itself has similar nail holes, but further apart. One can therefore be fairly sure that the lid came from another box; the patina is identical with that on the rest of the desk.

The real problem arises when we look at the date. This occupies the space where an original lock would have been, and there is a slot in the top of the front panel where one would expect the hasp to have come if the lock was still beneath it. Closer examination shows the date to have been carved on a piece of oak which has been most carefully inserted into the lock plate area. The carver imitated the execution of the lower initials "O.G." so accurately that they could well have been by the same hand. Furthermore the punched matting in the background to the date very

204

205

closely matches that in the rest of the front panel. The semicircular decorations on the top margin of the date area match those elsewhere in the box. The slightly crude strapwork of the main design is probably earlier than 1662. This is repeated on the sides of the desk.

If one assumes that the strapwork is earlier, a possible sequence of events emerges: after perhaps 30 years the lock is broken and removed and is replaced by the dated piece of oak. Subsequently, or perhaps at the same time, the original lid is broken and replaced with one from another box. We will never know the connection, if any, between "O.G." and the date. The initials are undoubtedly part of the original desk.

I am fairly convinced that the alterations to the desk took place within a short period, the patina on all the parts appears the same. One further mystery lies in the desk. It originally had a stand; the tops of the legs of this remain inside the desk. These are of beech, and I feel that an original stand would have been made of oak.

Part of the fascination of these early pieces of furniture lies in the amount of tampering they have received. I like this desk, but I am not sure that I have fathomed its history. The date after all, may not have been carved in 1662 either. Where this leads us I do not know. It is not a national commemorative date, so far as I can tell, the only thing to happen in that year was the change in the method of manufacturing coins, from hammering, to milling. This was hardly likely to have been celebrated on a desk.

My daughter found this box tucked away in the corner of a very up-market antique shop, of the sort with a 3" deep carpet and coded prices which are not revealed until the proprietor whispers them into your ear (causing, in this case, near paralysis.) Within earshot of the owner my daughter who is impetuous called out "Daddy, this one's got your initials on it, you must buy it!" and all hope of a discount fled out of the window.

I waited for the whole of a week before going back to buy it and did succeed in negotiating a painfully small discount but the box still cost me more than I would happily admit. To wait for a week hardly qualifies as an "impulse" buy, and without the initials I would probably still have bought it, it is an interesting item. Now that I have made myself forget how much it cost I can enjoy it. After all, some people part with huge sums of money to buy "personalized" number plates for their cars, by comparison this was a mild conceit.

The box is entirely made of elm, which disqualifies it from entry into the main section of this book. There are no clues to the date in the moulding, which is to section "H" on page 64 and could be of any period. The carving is shallow, and the depth of 10" probably puts it into the 18th century; it certainly has none of the features of an earlier piece.

The front panel shows what I like to believe are palm trees and coconuts of the South Seas variety. The side panels each carry a portrait of some aquatic creature who is obviously very happy indeed; could he be an elephant seal?

The colour of the box is that rich golden brown which only old elm acquires and is so rare as the timber has such a short "sell by" date due its attraction to wood-worm. Elm timber was available in quantity in past centuries, and I believe that many boxes must have been made with it originally, only to be eaten.

I would very much like to know who the other "T.C." was; I like to think that he was a sea-captain who had voyaged through the South Pacific taking his box with him. (Elm is very resistant to sea water.)

I have no data for this rare desk. It bears however an interesting date, 1681. The top moulding is very characteristic of the late 17th/early 18th Centuries, inverted this occurs as base moulding on some later boxes (see box no.34.) The chamfered bottom boards are also a late feature.

(Courtesy Combe Cottage Antiques)

Box no.51.

A superb coffre-bach of about 1720, in the Welsh Folk Museum. The gouged petals of the flowers, the tulips, and vase motifs also appear on boxes 40, 41, and 43. (No. 43 is dated 1719).

Box no.52.

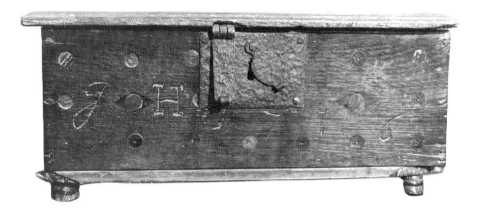

A small box dated 1716, with "berry" inlay in stained sycamore. The back board of this box has a group of narrower annual rings which could correlate with the dry summers of 1704, 1705, and 1706. (In the Welsh Folk Museum.)

Box no.53.

Line inlay on another small box; this also has double half-round applied moulding. Early 18th Century. (In the Welsh Folk Museum.)

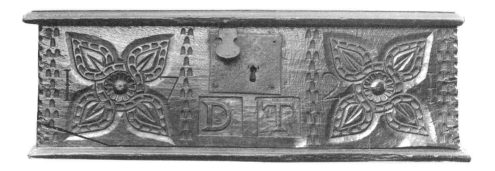

The Westcountry quatrefoil motif, also dated 1721 along the front panel. This date is almost certainly a later addition. This design is very similar in layout to box no. 28. (In the Welsh Folk Museum.)

A fine box with a contemporary date, 1723. (In the Welsh Folk Museum)

A superb desk with a contemporary date, 1635, and a heavily carved lid depicting two allegorical figures on each side of a lotus-flower. (In the Welsh Folk Museum)

This is a difficult box to date. Fleur-de-lis motifs have a long history, and I have seen carving very like this on a chair of about 1620. The box has an interesting lining paper however; consisting of the uncut sheets of pages from a book called "Astrological Judgements", these are for various months in 1653 and were over printed before entry into the box with what are obviously test "pulls" of a blackwork pattern, probably for embroidery. This lining paper probably sets the latest date for the box.

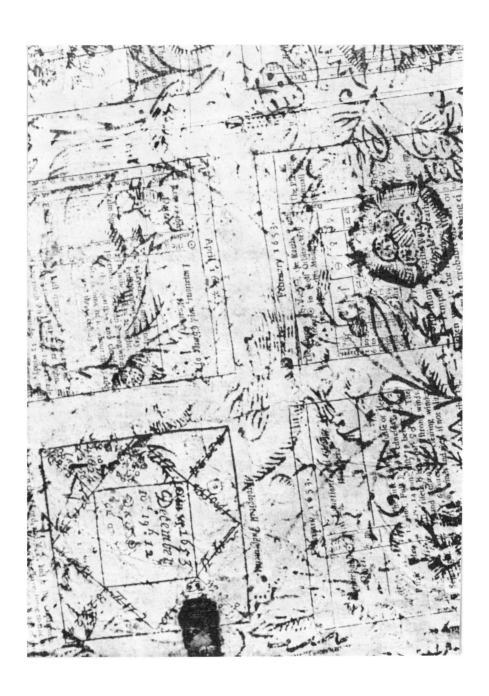

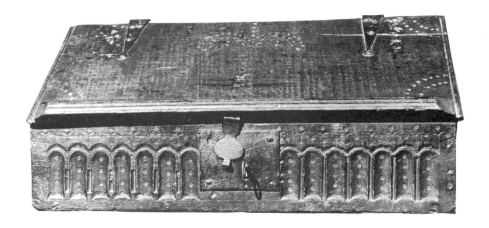

Another very early desk; I put this between 1600 and 1620. This truly a writing-desk, it has an applied batten on the lid to stop things sliding off. This carries the same half-round moulding as the rest of the lid. There is an interesting difference between the nulling on the left hand side and the right. Vertical grooves on the uprights between the nulling go half-way up on the left but all the way up on the right. This could be evidence for the prefabrication of long strips of carving which were then cross-cut to order. But if this is so, how does one explain the plain margins?

Box no.59

More guilloche ribbon decoration. This little desk also had stopped fluting on each side, and the early scratch block moulding around the top surfaces of the lid. The lock is probably the third, with a (broken) hinged cover to the keyhole and a brass insert around the hole. This present lock is probably Victorian; I have seen similar ones with "Patent" inscribed on the hinged cover. "Tudor" roses probably put the desk at about 1600.

Box no.60.

"Stopped" fluting on another early box, this is about 1600. (see box no.4.).
An Italian architect, Sebastiano Serlio illustrated an exact pattern in his
"Architectura" of 1611, although it occurs earlier in English woodwork.
Anthony Wells-Cole illustrates it (Regional Furniture 1990) in Brisley
Church Norfolk on panelling dated 1590.

Hinge types referred to in the text

A. External fishtail on box no. 8.   D. Strap/ring, (Welsh ?)

B. Flat fishtail.   E. Butterfly.

C. Round fishtail.   F. Ring.

The ink-and-wash cherub discovered hiding in box no.43. He seems quite pleased to have been let out. For some reason he is holding sprays of oak leaves, and I will let him end the book with them.

A.J. Conybeare.

GLOSSARY

Acanthus	A plant indigenous to the Mediterranean; the leaf shape of which appears as a Classical decorative motif, usually within another design.
Chamfer	A bevelled surface.
Cleft Oak	Oak logs split along the grain with a wedge or an axe to produce boards with a tapered section.
Coppice	A forestry system whereby many crops are harvested from the same roots upon an area by regularly cutting the stems which grow from them, at intervals determined by the size of the material required. Only applicable in the U.K. to certain hardwood species, particularly oak, sweet chestnut and ash, although hazel was important in many areas.
Coppice-with-standards	A coppice system where selected stems were left to grow into timber trees whilst the smaller stems were regularly harvested beneath them.
End-grain	The section of timber revealed by cutting across a board.
Epicormic buds	Small shoots which can appear upon otherwise clean stems of timber. They sometimes occur after too heavy a thinning operation when direct sunlight can reach the surface of the bark.
Escutcheon	Sometimes decorative plate at the front of a lock.
Fluting	See Nulling.
Guilloche	Classical motif in the form of a running ribbon, sometimes intertwined, usually with a floral centre. Found on wall decorations at Pompeii. See box no.5.
High Forest	A "modern" forestry system, whereby all the trees on an area are of the same age, forming a crop of roughly the same height.
Hoppus	Method of timber measurement still in use, based on ¼ circumference.
Lunette	A semi circular motif, usually with an infill of acanthus or palm leaves, sometimes a half-rose. See box no.24.
Mortice and tenon	A common joint for fixing two pieces of timber together at right angles to one another, the one slotting into the other.
Nulling	A decorative form resembling a railway viaduct with many arches, also known as fluting. See box no.9.
Ogee	A Classical moulding composed of two curves, in section shaped like an "S".

Overstorey	In forestry terms, the trees which have their crowns at the highest level in a plantation; standard oaks in a coppice area which have their crowns above the lower regrowth.
Ovolo	Convex Classical moulding profile, usually a full quarter of a circle in section.
Palmate	With the shape of a palm leaf.
Pedunculate oak	In an open situation tends to produce short butts and wide-spreading crowns, the branches of which were prized for "crooks" and "bends" for ship- and house-building. The trees have a stalked acorn.
Quarter-sawn	A method of cutting logs firstly into four segments along the grain then cutting boards from alternate faces of each segment, to expose the radial rays within the timber.
Quatrefoil	Design composed of four leaf shapes radiating from a common point.
Ring shake	A timber defect whereby a circular crack appears within the trunk, forming an inner cylinder within the tree.
Rotation	The period in years between felling operations upon an area.
Sessile oak	Produce longer clean lengths of timber than the pedunculate; the acorns sit on the twig.
Scratch-block	A home made tool which served as a primitive moulding plane, by scraping a simple profile into the timber.
Standard oak.	Those trees which were selected by reason of straightness and vigour to grow on in a coppice area to eventually produce timber.
Stopped fluting	Nulling with a vertical column running part-way up each groove. See box no.13.
Strapwork	Decorative Classical form usually derived from the "S" curve. See box no.16.
Sustained yield	The management of areas of forest so as not to cut in any period more than the increased increment put on by the trees during that period.
Understorey, Underwood	Coppice growth beneath standard trees intended for further periodic cutting for minor produce; smaller species such as hazel which are capable of growth in the shade of bigger trees.
Wildwood	Unmanaged "virgin" woodland which is self regenerating.